ELECTRIC KILN CONSTRUCTION FOR POTTERS

ELECTRIC KILN CONSTRUCTION FOR POTTERS

ROBERT FOURNIER

Photographs by John Anderson
Diagrams by Sheila Fournier

VNR VAN NOSTRAND REINHOLD COMPANY
New York Cincinnati Toronto London Melbourne

Acknowledgments

My sincere thanks to the following for their help and encouragement:

To Leslie Savage for checking the electrical sections and my calculations.

To Maurice Ball for ensuring that the Temperature Indicators and Controls section is accurate and sufficient.

To Peter Taylor for reading the manuscript and giving expert advice.

To Sheila for long hours of work on the diagrams.

To John Anderson for scientific advice and, of course, for the photographs which often tell more than words can.

To Frank Colson and M. Wikey for help with American equivalents and terminology.

To the many manufacturers and suppliers consulted.

Printed in the United States of America
Designed by Loudan Enterprise

Published in 1977 by Van Nostrand Reinhold Company
A division of Litton Educational Publishing, Inc.
450 West 33rd Street, New York, NY 10001, U.S.A.

Van Nostrand Reinhold Limited
1410 Birchmount Road, Scarborough, Ontario M1P 2E7
Canada

Van Nostrand Reinhold Australia Pty. Limited
17 Queen Street, Mitcham, Victoria 3132, Australia

Van Nostrand Reinhold Company Limited
Molly Millars Lane, Wokingham, Berkshire, England

16 15 14 13 12 11 10 9 8 7 6 5 4 3 2 1

Library of Congress Cataloging in Publication Data

Fournier, Robert C P
  Electric kiln construction for potters.

  Bibliography: p.
  Includes index.
  1. Kilns—Design and construction. I. Title.
TT924.F68 1977   681'.7666   76-54001
ISBN 0-442-30134-0

Contents

Preface

The aim of this book is to help potters build their own electric kilns: kilns which can be altered and balanced to a high state of efficiency. To this end it concentrates on principles which can be applied to many types and sizes of kiln. Some sample specifications are included but these are to be considered as guides to fulfilling your own requirements.

No specialist or mathematical skills are required; any potter should be able to construct a simple, but fully operational, pottery kiln.

For students and potters who do not intend to build their own equipment it is hoped that this book will help them to understand and appraise any electric kiln they may use.

Notes on Temperature and Dimensions

In order to save space and make for easier reading the following systems have been adopted throughout this book.

1. *Degrees of temperature* (°T) are given as Centigrade (Celsius)/Fahrenheit. For the higher values the Fahrenheit figure is given to the nearest 5 degrees.

EXAMPLES.
100/212°T
1300/2370°T

2. *Dimensions* are given as inches/millimeters and feet/meters.

EXAMPLES.
4.5/114mm
4.5/1.37m

3. The symbols for the *power of two and three*, X^2 and X^3, refer to area and volume respectively, not dimensions.

EXAMPLES.
A wall $2/0.186m^2$ indicates an area of 2 square feet or 0.186 square meters, *not* a wall with dimensions of 2 × 2 feet which would have an area of $4/0.37$ m^2. A kiln chamber of $2/0.057$ m^3 indicates 2 cubic feet of capacity *not* a cube with dimensions 2 × 2 × 2 feet.

Safety Notes

In any activity during which considerable amounts of energy are released there is an element of danger. The firing of pottery with any fuel comes into this category but, when used with common sense, an electric kiln is safer than most. If well insulated, electrically protected, and with the base raised at least 6/152mm from the floor, it can be used in any room in an ordinary house.

Rules to be observed include:

1. Do not switch the kiln on when packing or when the door or lid is wide open.

2. Ensure that all connections are cased in such a way that they cannot be touched, even accidentally.

3. Do not let children near the kiln when it is firing or cooling and see that they cannot energize the kiln in any way.

4. Take great care not to forget a kiln when it is on or to let it seriously overfire. If there is a danger of this happening, install a fail-safe control.

5. Ensure that all metal parts are adequately earthed.

6. Do not site a kiln in a place that is not fully weatherproof, or where it may get very damp.

7. Wooden floors and plastic tiles are safer than concrete as far as electric shock is concerned.

8. Ensure that the supply lines to, and within, your studio, are fully adequate to take the electrical load.

9. Do not leave combustible materials near the kiln when it is firing.

10. Take care, when peering through the spyhole, not to burn your hair. Do not open two spyholes at any one time.

11. When cutting or filing any inorganic material, e.g., metal, brick, and especially, asbestos, always wear a simple gauze mask. They are cheap and available from many drugstores and chemists. It is also a good rule never to eat, drink, or smoke when handling kiln materials—or any other pottery materials.

Introduction

Writers on electric kilns generally agree with Daniel Rhodes that "firings tend to be uniform with little variation in result." It has, however, been my experience that no two electric kilns behave exactly alike and that the precise quality of the product shows variety even in kilns which the potter has built, balanced, and fired many times.

While it is possible to obtain some measure of reduction, the natural atmosphere is oxidized or neutral. This does not mean that colors and glazes need lack interest. Reduction is often a danger in earthenware firing, while in the stoneware field, Shoji Hamada has produced a good deal of work in oxidation as have Lucie Rie, Hans Coper and others. The translucency of porcelain is not at all diminished. By the judicious use of wood ash and iron oxide, broken reds and blacks can be obtained which resemble, without imitation, temmoku glazes and the like. The oxides of copper, manganese, iron chromate, and other pigments which are largely ignored in reduction can be used with unique results. Reactions between fusible slips and glazes can be exploited.

It is also said that electric kilns are simple pieces of equipment and this is fundamentally true though some do not function at maximum efficiency. In many situations they are the only practical instruments for firing pottery. The electric kiln would not have been possible without the development of highly insulating, lightweight refractory bricks. The power input is not comparable to that of a fuelled kiln, and it must be used very efficiently.

For example, a 15 kW electric kiln with a chamber of $6/0.17m^3$ will develop about 50,000 Btu an hour. A gallon of oil produces around 130,000 Btu and an oil-fuelled kiln with an equivalent chamber might use 1.5 gallons an hour and produce approximately four times the heat input of the electric kiln. This point was illustrated in the case of an art school which became worried about the fumes given off during firing by certain clays, and so they installed vents and chimneys in their electric kilns. The kilns failed to reach maturing temperature with the vents open, no matter how long they were fired: the heat produced had come into balance with that escaping.

A tight, draft-free, insulated box is, therefore, the first necessity in building an electric kiln. Although less widely made by the industry, the top-loading kiln is the simplest construction with these qualities. The various types of kilns are discussed in Chapter 1. Within the box are housed wires, rods, or strips made of materials which will develop heat when electricity is passed through them. Provision must be made for supporting these conductors and keeping them apart.

The heat generated by the conductors or 'elements' is distributed by convection and conduction below 800/1470°T but the wire or rod will soon attain this temperature and the bulk of the heat dispersed is essentially radiant: it is given off in straight lines or rays from the surface of the element as distinct from combustible fuels which pour hot air and gases into the kiln. In a badly designed or very large kiln the effect may be to overfire those pots immediately facing the elements at the expense of those they shield from the radiant heat. In practice, conduction from one pot or piece of kiln furniture to another helps to distribute the heat but it remains an obvious advantage to have the heat sources spread as evenly and all-embracingly as possible. At the very least, two facing walls and the floor should be furnished with elements: ideally floor, four walls, and roof. In practice, three walls and floor of front-loaders, and four walls and floor of top-loaders, are the most common distributions. Because of its enclosed nature there is little convection of heat in the kiln chamber: the natural tendency of hot air to rise is frustrated by the fact that there is no cooler air to take its place. The top shelf is often the coolest place in the firing. Another consequence of radiant heat is that flat objects, such as plates, fire differently from upright pieces even though they may have identical body and glaze.

The proportions of the firing chamber will affect its performance; the heat loss through the walls being proportional to their surface area. The power (watts) needed to fire kilns of different sizes does not, therefore, increase arithmetically with an increase in volume but is related to the total wall area (including roof and floor). A cube is the perfect shape for minimum heat loss, a rectangular plan or elevation is more convenient for the packing of pots. The final design is always a compromise between these two considerations. In a very large kiln a rectangular plan is essential since two of the facing banks of elements must be within 30/760mm, or at most 3/0.9m, of one another.

The capacity limits are usually $0.5/0.014m^3$ to $60/1.7m^3$. Six to twenty cubic feet is the most common range. For high temperatures the one-to-three-cubic-foot range requires 3 kW per $1/0.03m^3$ decreasing to 1 kW per ft^3 at $30/0.84m^3$ and larger. See p. 43 for power/volume graphs. Kilowatt figures with values of about 0.7 of these may be substituted where temperatures are not to exceed 1125/2455°T.

The temperature reading in a kiln will always be lower than that of the elements themselves at the same moment. To obtain 1300/2370°T in the chamber, the element must be in the region of 1350/2460°T which is the absolute maximum for the most commonly used element wire, Kanthal A1. A top firing temperature of around 1280/2335°T is therefore recommended to allow this material a reasonably long life. Another factor is that the wire becomes soft at high temperatures and coils are liable to flop over onto one another. Luckily they develop an insulating oxide on the surface and the difference in electrical potential between neighboring coils is small. The wire also becomes thinner with use and so passes less current as it ages and the kiln takes longer to fire. Silicon-carbide rods allow greater temperatures—up to 1400/2550°T—and are increasingly coming into use. Rods are also prone to increasing resistance with age and, since they have a very long life, special provisions to maintain power need to be made.

Briefly, then, an electric kiln is a totally enclosed refractory box housing one or more circuits of a resistance material which is spread as evenly as possible over its inner surfaces.

I. Types of Electric Kilns

There are three common designs of electric kilns: the front-loader, the top-loader, and the sectional kiln. Found much less often in pottery studios are trolley kilns, and 'top-hat' kilns. Each kiln type has its advantages and drawbacks.

FRONT-LOADER

This is the most common industrially designed kiln. It has few disadvantages as a piece of equipment for firing: the chamber is usually of a convenient height for packing, and it is possible to furnish every inner face with elements. Difficulty can be experienced in packing heavy wares or shelves in the back of the kiln if the chamber is a deep one, and there is always the problem of ascertaining how near one pot is to the one behind it. The top of the kiln is usually too high for convenient use in stacking pots to dry, and the whole construction takes up a lot of room in an average studio.

The major engineering problem is the provision of a door, which should have the same insulation as the rest of the kiln. This door may be heavy and the initial snug fit is liable to be lost as the hinge wears and the door sags. There is often some insulation failure at the top and bottom sections. A built-up wall which is dismantled at each firing is an easier solution for the amateur builder, but no door elements can then be accommodated. With the development of lightweight insulators, the door is becoming less of an obstacle.

Racks beneath the chamber can be useful for drying or storage. The space above and below front-loading kilns is too seldom put to good use.

TOP-LOADER

There are few industrial top-loaders supplied for stoneware temperatures (they are more common in the U.S.) although they can be very efficient in this range. They are usually supplied in a rather lightly built form, with a thin, hinged lid.

For the builder, who does not need more than about 14/0.4 m^3 capacity, however, this is the type to try. It has several advantages: it is easier to house elements in four walls and floor; pots can be placed very close together since the plan of the pack is always visible; whether idling or firing, the table-height top can be utilized for drying or as a working surface. The top does not need a boxed-up lid; slabs or bricks can be laid over the roof at each firing in a few minutes.

Because there is no permanent roof to be supported, this type can be dismantled or altered. There are certain difficulties in housing elements very near the top of the walls since the soft insulating brick used in electric kilns is liable to be damaged by the roof bats if too thin a section is left above the uppermost element (see Diag. 45). Chamber height is limited to about 24/610 mm.

SECTIONAL TOP-LOADING KILN

Until recently these could not be recommended for the professional potter but the development of super-efficient lightweight insulators have increased their value and range. A strap-bound, hexagonal plan is common. The insulation appears to be dangerously thin on some commercial models. The design is probably most useful for lower-temperatures wares—raku, enamels, and terracotta firings of tall sculptural pieces.

Ill. 1. The author unpacking a small top-loading kiln.

Ill. 2. A typical heavily built, British commercial front-loader, Model L11 HT by Kilns and Furnaces Ltd. (Photo: Kilns and Furnaces Ltd.)

Ill. 3. A top-loading kiln built and used by the author for many firings.

14

TROLLEY KILN

A trolley kiln is a type of front-loader in which the ware is packed on a wheeled platform which is then trundled into the firing chamber which may be open at both ends. Its advantage in a pottery with a large and continuous output is that a second trolley can be loaded while the first is firing. One needs some experience in simple engineering to construct a kiln of this type. It is possible to obtain continuous kiln trucks at scrap prices which are still quite suitable for this application. A gas-fired kiln described by Frank Colson in *Kiln Building with Space-Age Materials* could be adapted. Peter Taylor of Labheat, England, has designed a two-part truck with integral walls which is briefly described and illustrated on pp. 89–90.

TOP-HAT KILN

In a top-hat kiln the ware is packed as in a trolley kiln but the chamber is lowered over it from above. Weight is the key factor: with conventional brick construction considerable power is needed to lift virtually the whole kiln over the pack, while precise control is essential in lowering it. Considerable studio ceiling height would also be required. In industry the top-hat is used for large porcelain insulators and the like where the ware is more difficult to move than the kiln itself! Only the use of very light and efficient insulators for hot-face situations can bring the electric top-hat kiln within the range of the potter-builder. Such refractories are obtainable but not yet fully proved in practice. See pp. 39–40.

2. Types of Elements

It is unfortunate that the word 'element' has come to describe the heating equipment in a fire or kiln: unfortunate because it has several other meanings and is therefore imprecise. Confusion also arises from the fact that a single element can comprise a whole circuit or only a section of a circuit. In either case an element consists of a length of electrical resistance material which can conveniently be housed in the kiln chamber. From each end of the element extend leads or 'tails', ideally of a less resistant material, which pierce the kiln walls so that they may be connected to other elements or to the mains supply on the outside of the kiln. This is necessitated by the fact that there is, as yet, no generally practical way of joining elements on the hot-face.

The two main types of elements are wire coils and silicon-carbide rods. In addition, metal alloy resistance material may take the form of 'tape' or strip.

WIRE COILS AND TAPE

Resistance wire is made in several grades each with its maximum firing temperature. The element temperature of nickel-chrome-iron alloys ranges up to 1200/2190°T. As this is always 40–50/70-85°T greater than that in the kiln chamber, their working limit is nearer 1150/2100°T, suitable for earthenware or enamel kilns.

The more heat-resistant alloys of iron, chromium, cobalt, and aluminum are the most commonly used in kilns. There is also a superwire of molybdenum-disilicide which will fire up to 1600/2900°T but, in addition to its high cost, its use poses mechanical problems which put it outside the range of any but well-equipped industrial plants. The largest manufacturer is Kanthal of Sweden. The wire is sold under license in various parts of the world. There are also comparable wires known as Alchrome from Germany and Pyrox from Japan.

Kanthal A grade has an operating ceiling of 1250/2280°T (1300/2370° element temperature); Kanthal A1 grade, 1300/2370°T (1350/2460° element temperature). For a reasonable life expectancy, however, it is advisable to subtract 20/35°T from these figures.

Resistance tape requires corrugating and welding tools and, for thicknesses above 1.5 mm, heating to 250/420°T before bending. Resistance wire of any gauge up to 13 Standard Wire Gauge (swg) or 11 American Wire Gauge (awg, which corresponds to the B & S—Brown & Sharp—gauge as given in the Kanthal Handbook) can be wound on simple homemade apparatus. The gauge numbers indicate cross-sectional diameters, starting at No. 0 for the thickest (0 swg is 0.324 in. in diameter) to the other extreme at 47 swg (0.002 in. diameter). The two-gauge systems swg and awg do not correspond but certain sizes (e.g., 13 swg and 11 awg, 14 swg and 12 awg, 15 swg and 13 awg) are close enough to be bracketed together for many practical purposes. Coiled-wire elements of Kanthal A or A1 grade are the most widely used in potters' kilns and are the easiest of the metal-based resistance materials to handle. At this time it is still a relatively cheap material.

Coiled elements are referred to as straight or hairpin and occasionally double hairpin. It would be possible to extend a hairpin over more than three slots but, except for very thin gauges, it would be physically very difficult to place it in the slots without one or more sections springing out. Very long elements extending round four sides of a kiln are sometimes used: these need extralong winding rods and have other problems associated with them.

Metal elements are liable to sudden burn-out and are attacked by most reducing agents (exceptions, hydrogen and cracked ammonia). Supply gas and the usual hydrocarbons will reduce element life. See pp. 110-111.

16

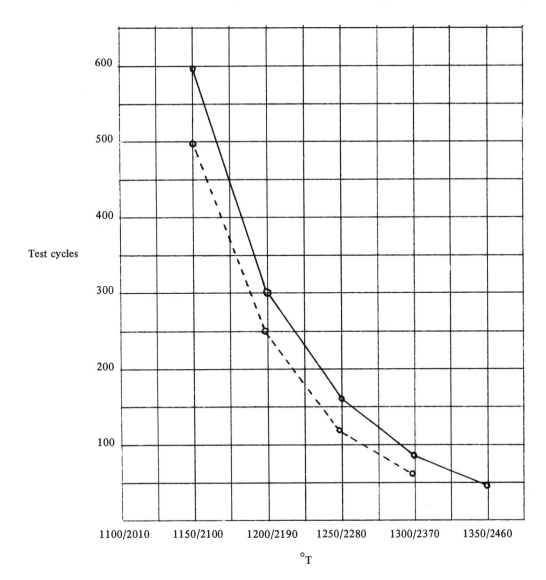

| °T | 1100/2010 | 1150/2100 | 1200/2190 | 1250/2280 | 1300/2370 | 1350/2460 |

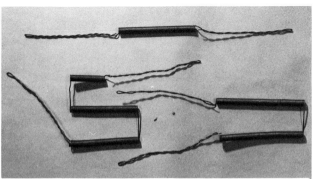

Ill. 4. Straight, double hairpin, and hairpin elements, close-wound. These would be stretched to about 2.5 times their present length for use in the kiln.

Graph 1. Life Diagram of Kanthal Alloys. Solid line, Kanthal A1; dotted line, A. The figures refer to *wire temperature:* chamber temperature would be about 40/72°T lower. N.B. The 1970 Kanthal Handbook gives a more optimistic assessment of probable life but, if the left-hand figures are taken as number of firings, the above graph corresponds more closely to my experience of coiled elements.

SILICON-CARBIDE ROD

Silicon, SiC, in the form of hollow or solid rods can be used as elements. They are made in a great variety of sizes, normally as straight rods but also as U shapes. They are self-supporting if properly selected for their placement. Certain clearances are required so that the rod can disperse the heat produced. They will endure up to 1600/2900°T; have a long life; and are less affected than wire by reducing atmospheres, especially if the dense, glazed type is used. On the other hand their initial cost is many times that of wire; they are less flexible in their positioning; they are brittle and must be protected against accidental blows; and they pose certain design problems in front-loading kilns.

The high-resistance rods are hollow; low-resistance rods are solid. Their performance has been greatly improved since their introduction in the 1930s. Although many of the standard rods still require a voltage transformer for efficient use, the denser types can be powered directly from a 240 V supply.

The temperature range of SiC rods far surpasses that of wire elements. As previously mentioned, however, their cost is currently between six and twenty times that of a comparable set of Kanthal Al elements. This initial expense could possibly be recouped in time owing to their longer life—up to 4,000 hours when treated with care—and greater reliability at high temperatures. A potter's reduction cycle will impose very little strain on them. Their lack of flexibility in heat-spread through the kiln is not helped by the considerable increase in price for rods over 18/458 mm long.

The typical rod has three sections: the outer or end sections which penetrate the kiln wall are metal coated and offer much less resistance than the operative central section, so that energy is not wasted on heating the kiln walls and brickwork.

Rods are also made with both connections at one end, and as U shapes equivalent to the hairpin coiled element, which can be supported from the roof or stand out horizontally from the back wall of the kiln. These special types are expensive.

There are other methods of heating a kiln which are not immediately relevant to this book and are mentioned here, therefore, only briefly. Elements of platinum alloys which are virtually indestructible are used (under strict security!) for very high temperatures in special industrial kilns. Molybdenum wire can be wound round a ceramic tube and surrounded by a reducing atmosphere within a gas-tight, insulating case. Current can also be passed through a copper tube wound as a coil, which is cooled by a flow of water through it. This sets up a magnetic field which produces heat in a carbon or iron inductor. Temperatures up to 2500/4500°T can be readily reached by this means in a few minutes, and cooled as quickly. This system is also used to kill weevils in flour, but at a lower temperature!

Kiln elements are discussed in detail in Chapter 6.

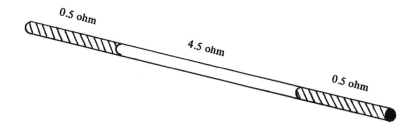

Diag. 1. SiC rods have outer sections (which pierce the kiln walls) that have lower resistance and therefore less heat-generation than the operative central section.

3. Electricity

PRINCIPLES

For the purposes of this book a simplified version of the theory of electrical power is sufficient. The outer electrons of some materials, typically metals, have a certain freedom of movement across interatomic spaces. Electricity is a form of energy applied to these materials which changes the random movement of the 'free' electrons into a drift in one direction. As the number of electrons in free motion increases, the number of electron collisions also increases and heat is generated. Where the 'flow' of electricity is impeded to only a small degree, the material is a *conductor*; if to a somewhat greater degree it is known as a *resistance* material; if electrical flow is completely obstructed it is an *insulator* or non-conductor.

The wires and connectors feeding a kiln or other electrical apparatus stretch all the way back to the power-station and so must have maximum conductivity. They are composed of copper or aluminum. The heating elements in a kiln are made of alloys or other compounds which conduct and yet resist electrical flow and so become hot in the process. All other parts of the kiln in any contact with wires, connectors, or elements must be effective insulators.

For electrical current to flow through a conductor a connection must be made between the source of electrical pressure and a 'negative' terminal or 'earth'. The source of electrical pressure is known as the 'live' or 'positive' terminal or wire (in mains supplies called the 'line' or 'hot wire', symbol L), the negative terminal may be represented by the 'neutral' (N) or 'earth' (E) which is literally the damp subsoil of the ground. Such a connection forms a *circuit*.

As soon as a circuit is established, electricity begins to flow in amounts controlled by the degree of resistance exerted by the material of the circuit. If, therefore, a length of highly conductive metal is placed across the terminals, current can flow in almost unlimited quantities but since no material is 100-percent conductive, somewhere along the circuit the wire will heat up until it melts or sets adjoining matter ablaze. This is known as a short circuit.

A circuit must, therefore, also include a section of resistance material which will allow only a limited amount of current to pass. This may be used to set up a magnetic field as in a motor; or produce energy in the form of heat as in a light bulb (a white-hot wire), a fire, or an electric kiln.

To guard against the accidental development of a short circuit, a weak link of easily melted wire enclosed in a fire-proof casing—called a *fuse*—is always introduced into the circuit. The fuse will fail immediately as an excess of current begins to flow and so breaks the continuity of the circuit.

It is obvious that some means must be provided whereby the circuit can be opened or closed at will, i.e., a *switch*. The basic components of a circuit are: conducting wires, switch mechanisms, resistance equipment, and fuse. More complete details of circuit installations are given in Chapter 7.

When electricity is drawn from a battery or accumulator the flow is continuous in one direction between the positive and negative terminals. This is known as *direct current* (d.c.). However it has been found that certain technical advantages can be derived by using a system whereby the direction of flow of electricity is subject to rapid reversals and it is supplied in this form on most mains installations. This is called *alternating current* (a.c.). The rapidity of the alternations, or the *frequency* of the supply, is indicated by cycles per second. In Britain the frequency is a standard 50 cycles; in the U.S., usually 60 cycles. Except for electric motors this divergence does not affect calculations. One aspect of alternating current however, is that connections can be made between two lines instead of line and neutral. When this is done the voltage is increased.

TABLE 1
Electrical Properties of Some Commonly Used Materials

Good Conductors	Resistance Materials	Good Insulators
metals, especially: copper, aluminum, iron, tin, silver	Kanthal and other trade names of especially prepared wire and strip	clay, dry or fired, hence bricks, etc., and most clays
impure water	silicon carbide (SiC)	minerals
wet materials, in general	molten glass	cold glass or glaze
		rubber
		most plastics
		distilled water
		hardwoods
		mineral wool and ceramic fiber
		ebonite
		asbestos
		NOTE: The insulation value of materials will vary with temperature. See p. 84.

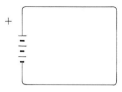

Diag. 2. Circuit.

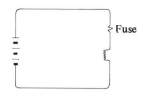

Diag. 4. Circuit with resistance and fuse.

Diag. 3. Circuit with resistance.

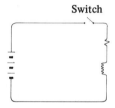

Diag. 5. Fuse and switch are always inserted in the line side of the resistance, never in the neutral.

20

ELECTRICAL UNITS

Various aspects and physical quantities have been isolated and defined in order to describe and deal with electrical flow. You need to understand four basic factors. Each has been given two international symbols, one for the factor itself and one for its unit of measurement. They are as follows:

1. The *pressure* or *electromotive force* (E) behind the flow is measured in units called *volts* (V). Pressure can vary in degree from the harmless flashlight battery at around 2 V to the 33,000 V or more in overhead cables, which could shrivel a man to death. Household voltages ranges from 110 V to 240 V. Both can be lethal.

2. The degree of *resistance* (R) to the passage of current is measured in *ohms* (Ω). This is the only symbol which is not a letter of the Roman alphabet.

3. The flow of *current* (I) is measured in *amperes* (A).

4. The rate of energy transfer, or *power* (P) has the unit *watt* (W). As this is a small unit and kilns run at thousands of watts, the thousand is usually replaced by the letter k (kilo) as in "a 5 kW kiln." The amount of electricity consumed in an hour is the basis for pricing supply; the power of 1,000 watts continuously for one hour, or 1 kWh, is the unit used for pricing supply.

Each factor is related to and controls the value of the others. A number of permutations of simple multiplication and division link them in such a way that, if any two are known, the others can be deduced. Using the symbols above we can state the following:

$$I = \frac{P}{E}$$

The same equation stated in terms of the measurement units would read: current in amperes equals power in watts divided by pressure in volts. Similarly, bringing resistance into the picture:

$$I = \frac{E}{R}$$

or, current in amperes equals pressure in volts divided by resistance in ohms. By transposing the first equation symbols:

$$P = I \times E$$

or, power in watts equals amperes times volts. By substitution we can get:

$$P = \frac{E}{R} \times E$$

(the second and third equations used together) which can also be written as:

$$P = \frac{E^2}{R}$$

The reference chart below gives the full range of relationships. In fact numbers one and two above express the whole scheme and all the rest say the same thing in different ways and are used purely for convenience in calculations. You do not need to do more than accept the relationships and work them out as practical numbers by simple arithmetic. With the aid of a small electronic calculator you can do this in a few seconds.

TABLE 2
Unit Relationships

$E =$	$I \times R$	$\dfrac{P}{I}$	$\sqrt{P \times R}$
$I =$	$\dfrac{P}{E}$	$\dfrac{E}{R}$	$\sqrt{\dfrac{P}{R}}$
$R =$	$\dfrac{E}{I}$	$\dfrac{E^2}{P}$	$\dfrac{P}{I^2}$
$P =$	$\dfrac{E^2}{R}$	$E \times I$	$I^2 \times R$

21

EXAMPLE 1.

How many amperes of current are needed to produce 6 kW on a 110 V supply?

Using $I = \dfrac{P}{E}$, $\dfrac{6000 \text{ (W)}}{110 \text{ (V)}} = 54.5$ amperes

EXAMPLE 2.

How many ohms of resistance are needed to obtain 6 kW on a 110 V supply? This can be worked out in two stages by arriving at the amperes of current as above, then:

$\dfrac{E}{I} = R$, $\dfrac{110}{54.5} = 2.01$ ohms

or in one stage using $\dfrac{P}{I^2} = R$ $\dfrac{6000}{54.5^2} = \dfrac{6000}{2960} = 2.01$

EXAMPLE 3.

You have a supply of 30 A at 240 V. What is the maximum power you can safely draw?

Using $P = I \times E$, $30 \times 240 = 7200$ W, or 7.2 kW

As previously mentioned, all materials, even when classed as very good conductors, put up some resistance to electrical flow. The degree of resistance is cumulative, that is if a foot length of wire exerts X ohms, then 100 feet will exert $100X$ ohms. Resistance is lessened if the current has a thicker gauge of wire to flow through—a situation roughly analogous to water flowing through smaller or larger bore pipes. It follows that, if you conduct current to an apparatus by means of too thin a wire, not only will the wire get hot and dangerous but some of the force will be spent before the supply reaches the equipment resulting in a drop in voltage and consequent inefficient performance. For a given amount of power required, the lower the supply voltage the thicker the feed wires need to be to avoid heating or voltage drop. See Chapter 7 for a list of recommended wire thicknesses required for given current flows.

For elements, wire is especially prepared from high-temperature alloys which exert a specific resistance resulting in heat energy. For each gauge and type of wire the resistance is constant at a given temperature. It is usual to state the resistance (in ohms) per foot/meter of length at 16/60°T. Resistance increases slightly with temperature. The full tables for Kanthal wire, etc. will be found in Table 14 on p. 115 of this book. It will be seen that the values for A1 wire range from 0.103 ohms per foot for 13 swg to 0.38 ohms per foot for the thinner 18 swg.

The equations discussed in this chapter can be used to work out element circuits once the ohms per foot/meter figure has been established. This is considered in detail in the calculation section of Chapter 6, but one example can be given to illustrate the possibilities.

EXAMPLE 4.

We are to use 120 feet of 13 swg A1 wire as a single circuit. This will exert 0.103 ohms per foot. $120 \times 0.103 = 12.4$ ohms total. What power will be produced by this circuit?

(a) On 240 volts supply $\left(\dfrac{E}{R} = I\right)$: $\dfrac{240}{12.4} = 19.4$ amperes
$(E \times I = P)$ $240 \times 19.4 = 4656$ watts or 4.656 kW.

(b) On a 120 volts supply $\left(\dfrac{E}{R} = I\right)$: $\dfrac{120}{12.4} = 9.7$ amperes
$9.7 \times 120 = 1164$ watts or 1.164 kW.

Note the comparatively small amount of power from 110 V which necessitates special planning of the elements.

There are, of course, many more factors involving sophisticated mathematics associated with the science of electrical engineering, but those discussed above are the essential units and equations needed to work out the wiring for a potter's kiln.

SERIES AND PARALLEL CIRCUITS

The individual lengths of resistance wire or rod in a kiln may be connected to form one circuit, or may constitute two or more circuits. If, for example, three elements are connected as in Diagram 6, they form one continuous circuit between line and neutral and the connection is then known as *series*, i.e., the elements form one group or series. The resistance of the circuit will be the total of all three lengths of wire. If, however, the same three elements are connected each to line and neutral, as in Diagram 7, they are said to be wired in *parallel* and the current can flow through all three simultaneously. This will reduce the resistance compared with the series wiring, with a corresponding increase in the current flowing and the heat generated.

If the 120 feet of 13 swg wire in Example 4 were split into three 40-foot lengths and these were wired in series the calculations in that Example would apply: 4656 W on 240 V. Connecting the three 40-foot lengths in parallel, however, means that each length exerts only approximately

4 ohms of resistance, and the current passed is $\left(\dfrac{E}{R} \times 3 = I\right)$: $\dfrac{240}{4}$ per length $\times$ 3 lengths = 180 amperes or $(I \times E = P)$ 180 $\times$ 240 = 43.2 kW. This is nine times the power compared with the same elements in series. If this example were used in practice the wire would, of course, almost immediately melt.

On a 120 V supply the parallel calculations give a more realistic conclusion: $\dfrac{E}{R} = \dfrac{120}{4} = 30$ amp $\times$ 3 = 90 amperes or 10.8 kW of power.

In kilns with more than one circuit the wiring is a combination of series and parallel. See Diagram 8. A further discussion and tables of kiln wiring for various voltages is given in Chapter 6.

It might be thought that lower voltages would mean cheaper and easier installation but a glance at the following Example will show that the reverse is the case because of the high current rating which involves the use of much thicker feed wires.

EXAMPLE 5.
To obtain 5 kW of power:

on 240 volts $\dfrac{5000}{240} = 20.8$ amperes of current

on 120 volts $\dfrac{5000}{120} = 41.6$ amperes of current

Diag. 6. Three elements forming series circuit.

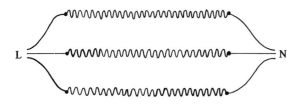

Diag. 7. Three elements forming parallel circuit.

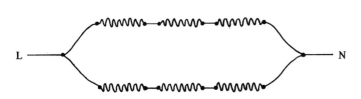

Diag. 8. Two ways of indicating two circuits of three elements each, involving both series and parallel connections.

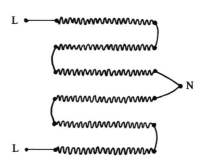

VOLTAGE DROP

The foregoing examples illustrate the effects of different voltages. These can be accommodated in the design of the elements. Occasionally, however, more current is drawn from the supply than the generating stations can cope with and the pressure, or voltage, will fall. This occurs at peak periods of demand such as late afternoon in winter, in very cold weather, when generators are out of action, or even when millions of people switch on a favorite television program! This effect is known as a 'brown out' in the U.S.

It needs only a small percentage drop in voltage seriously to effect lights and heating apparatus, especially when input is near the optimum requirement as in most kilns.

EXAMPLE 6.
A 240 V kiln rated at 15 kW:

$$\frac{15000}{240} = 62.5 \text{ amperes}$$

$$\frac{240}{62.5} = 3.84 \text{ ohms}$$

If the 240 V drops to 220 V: Power $= \dfrac{220^2}{3.84} = 12.6$ kW

Thus an 8-percent voltage drop results in 16 percent less power. Voltage drop may also result from inefficient installation, generally where a long feed from the meter to the kiln is involved. A long lead will always involve *some* resistance although, if it is of thick enough wire, this will be small. The voltage at the kiln point can be checked by an electrician and any fall accommodated in the calculations of the elements. The Table 13 on p. 114 lists recommended gauges for various loads.

PHASES

So far, to avoid confusion, a single-line-plus-neutral supply has been assumed. The mains electric supply which feeds an area from a substation, however, is carried on four cables: three separate lines and one neutral (sometimes, in the U.S., three lines to earth). It is important, because of the method of generation, to keep a balance between the current flowing in each line or 'phase'. Normally, for domestic, use, a branch from line one would be fed into a house, branches from lines two and three into its neighbors, returning to line one for the fourth house and so on. Each house would then be on a *single-phase* supply. If one of the buildings was a factory, this would lead to an imbalance of demand and so branches from all *three phases* would be wired in. Simi-

larly the supply company might insist that a kiln taking more than about 60 amperes of current should consist of three circuits each connected to one phase thus keeping the demand in balance. Less often two phases are brought in.

The cable used in a domestic installation will usually cope with about 60 amperes of current but this will include lights, heating, cooker (25 A and more) and so on. Often there is insufficient spare capacity for a kiln should most of the other items be in use simultaneously. A very small kiln of about 3.5 kW is equivalent to two two-bar electric fires and usually poses no problem. Overloaded cables can, however, cause fires and the advice of an electrician should be sought before connecting any appliance rated over 3kW.

A circuit on a single phase is complete when a line has an unbroken passage back to neutral. Three phases can give each line a separate circuit, all three being fed back to neutral. On each phase the voltage will be similar to that on a single phase supply, i.e., 240 V in Great Britain, often 110 or 120 V elsewhere. It is possible, of course, to take three circuits from a single phase but the load on the line will then be the total of all three. Voltage remains unaltered. See Diagrams 9, 10, and 11. Note: The resistance symbols in these diagrams represent the total resistance material in a circuit which will almost certainly be split into several elements in a kiln.

If, instead of connecting line to neutral, a circuit is made *between lines* the voltage across the circuit is thereby increased, from 240 to 415 V in the U.K. and from 120 to 240 V in the U.S. The two types of connections are known as *star* (lines to neutral) and *delta* (line to line).

The greatly increased voltage across lines must, of course, be considered when working out element resistance: very different figures emerge from calculations. The higher voltages, especially the 240/415 British standard, increase the danger of shock and short circuit. The system is not often used at 415 V for wire elements but is useful for adapting to the increase of resistance with age of silicon-carbide rods. See the system worked out by Peter Taylor on p. 84. In America the system is more common in order to obtain a 240 V supply. When this is done the neutral is 'grounded' (earthed) to the case of the kiln. See Chapter 7.

When three-phase supplies are connected, the installation charge for material is obviously going to be at least twice that for a line and neutral. Each cable will often rate 100 amperes or more.

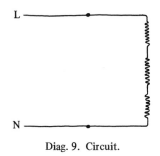

Diag. 9. Circuit.

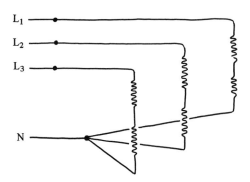

Diag. 10. Three-phase circuit.

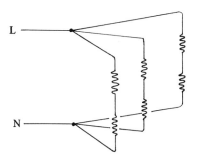

Diag. 11. Three circuits, one phase.

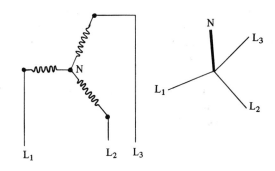

Diag. 12. Star connections, lines to neutral, can also be illustrated as in Diagram 10.

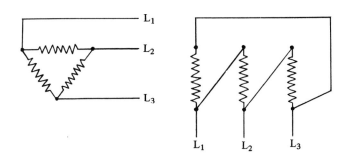

Diag. 13. Two ways of indicating delta connections across phases (U.K.). This wiring will give increased voltage compared with star. The normal British supply is 415/240 V: 415 V across phases; 240 V line to neutral. In the U.S. two 120 V lines are connected to a given 240 V supply.

WIRE GAUGES

The 'gauge' is the cross-sectional diameter of a wire. Resistance wires of the same metal alloys will have similar characteristics but the degree of resistance will vary with the gauge. The smaller the diameter of the wire the less current will flow compared with the same length of wire of a different gauge. This can be considered as roughly analogous to the effect of different sized bores of water-pipe—the smaller the pipe, the less quantity of water can flow through it for a given pressure.

Conversely, as has been discussed previously, a long wire will put up more resistance to electrical flow and thus pass less current (and produce less power) than a shorter one.

The letters swg in Table 3 refer to Standard Wire Gauge.

There is also a B & S (Brown & Sharp) series which corresponds to awg, American Wire Gauge. Both have a logical sequence but the increments between diameters are different and one scale rarely corresponds to the other. In each case, the thinner the wire, the higher the number. No. 0 swg has a diameter of 0.32/8.12 mm; 47 swg, 0.002/0.051 mm. These are the extremes and the midway potter's range is shown in Table 3. Because of the confusion of gauges, wire is often quoted in terms of its diameter, a somewhat clumsier and less immediately recognizable figure. The swg dimensions also apply to the thicknesses of metal sheet.

For copper conductors a nominal cross-sectional area in mm^2 is now used in place of gauge numbers. See Table 13 in Chapter 7.

TABLE 3
Resistance Wire Gauges

Gauge	No.	(Diameter) Inches	Millimeters	
SWG	11	0.116	2.946	Can be wound on a lathe
AWG	9	0.114	2.906	Suitable for any temperature
SWG	12	0.104	2.642	
AWG	10	0.102	2.588	Possible, but difficult to hand-wind
SWG	13	0.092	2.337	Thickest wire easily wound by hand
AWG	11	0.091	2.304	
AWG	12	0.081	2.052	Recommended for stoneware
SWG	14	0.080	2.032	
AWG	13	0.072	1.829	Can be used for stoneware, but marginal
SWG	15			
AWG	14	0.064	1.628	Can be used for earthenware and enamels (decals)
SWG	16	0.064	1.626	
AWG	15	0.057	1.450	
SWG	17	0.056	1.422	Too thin for most pottery uses
AWG	16	0.051	1.290	
SWG	18	0.048	1.219	

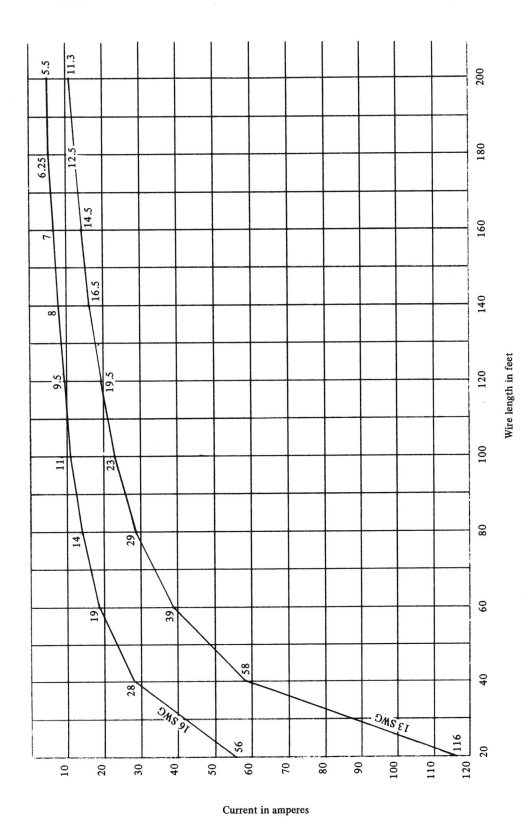

Graph 2. Current passed by Kanthal A1 wire, 13 and 16 swg, at 240 V.

COST

The basic unit for pricing electricity is kilowatt-hour, or kWh, which is equal to one kilowatt of power used for one hour. The cost of this unit may vary greatly, and is based on the desire of the suppliers to encourage or deter the use of electricity at any particular time. The amount of energy bought per kWh, however is always the same. Electricity cannot be stored. When many industrial users have closed down—late at night or on weekends—therefore, there is an excess of production over consumption and the cost of electricity per unit is generally priced most cheaply at these times.

It is recommended that you ask your power supplier for details of *all* the rates applicable to your region. Sometimes rates normally applicable to farmers or commercial premises may be advantageous to the potter. Some are based on a maximum-load charge and these are rarely economical, being geared to continuous processes and relatively high consumption. Other rates may specify only night consumption (sometimes only seven or eight hours duration), or night and weekend use, or summer and winter variations.

A rate for limited hours may operate on a switch-off time-clock system which means that your firing will come to a premature end if not completed in time, or a change-over time-clock system which does not shut off, but switches to a more expensive rate. Be careful that you thoroughly understand the eventual cost of current supplied under any particular rate system.

Once the price per kWh has been established it is a simple matter to work out the cost of a firing, which is: unit cost times kW rating of kiln times hours of firing.

EXAMPLE 7.
Unit cost per kWh = $.07
Kiln rating = 15.5 kW
Cost of firing for 1 hour = $.07 × 15.5 = $1.08
Cost of a $9\frac{1}{2}$ hour firing = $.07 × 15.5 × 9.5 = $10.26

This principle works whether you are on single- or three-phase supply, but it refers only to the kiln firing at full power. If, for instance, it is fired at an average of 50 percent on a controller or at a medium-switch rating, you can obtain an approximation of the cost by halving the number of hours over which the control operates.

EXAMPLE 8.
Average power (50%) for 6 hours and full power for 7 hours is equivalent to 3 + 7 = 10 hours at full power.

Another way of checking the cost of a firing is to read the meter before and after the firing, substract one figure from the other and multiply by the unit cost.

EXAMPLE 9.
Meter reading at switch-on   17436
Meter reading at switch-off 17543
Units used: 543 - 436 = 107
107 × $.07 (or whatever the unit cost) = $7.49

Depending on your power supplier you may be charged a fee in addition to the unit cost. For example, customers of Con Edison in the U.S. must pay a fuel-adjustment charge (a percentage of the total cost of kWh used). In the U.K. a standing charge may be made irrespective of the current used to help cover capital costs of supply. The extra amount this puts on the cost of a firing cannot be ascertained until you know how many firings are likely to be completed. Divide the charge by the number of firings, and add this figure to that obtained above.

By reading the meter hourly you can also check the correct functioning of the kiln. The units 'consumed' should correspond to within 10 percent of the kiln rating in kW.

It is a valuable exercise, in order to check your profitability, to estimate the value of a kiln load and to work out what percentage of this value the combined biscuit and glaze firing has cost you. It is unlikely that the firing has cost you less than 2 percent but is should not be more than 5 percent.

4. Heat and Insulation

In scientific terms heat is defined as a form of energy possessed by a substance when its atoms or molecules are in a state of random movement. All substances, at temperatures above absolute zero, have some heat energy. The mass, temperature, and heat capacity of a material determine the amount of this energy present. The heat may be transmitted by conduction, contact, convection, and radiation. Heat is initially emitted in an electric kiln by radiation, thereafter by conduction and contact; very little heat is emitted by convection wherein an electric kiln differs fundamentally from a fueled kiln.

Heat will always 'flow' from an object of higher temperature to one of lower temperature. The heat produced in an electric kiln is transferred to the pots, shelves, and wall of the kiln, and through the walls to the outer air. Two of the main objects of kiln design are to conduct the heat from the elements to the pots as efficiently as possible, and to minimize conduction through the thickness of the kiln walls.

DEFINITIONS AND EXAMPLES

Conduction, or the rate at which heat is transmitted from one face of a block of material to another one, is more rapid through dense, heavy materials than light, porous ones: Metals will, in general, conduct heat faster than non-metals or metal-oxide compounds. Denser material will also have a greater capacity for storing heat, i.e., more energy is needed to raise its temperature.

Diag. 14.

A. *Convection*. Air, when heated, rises and cooler air flows in to take its place. Convection occurs only to a small extent inside an electric kiln but is a factor in heat loss from the outside face of the kiln.

B. *Radiation*. Heat is given off from hot element surface to pots, kiln furniture, and walls and at higher temperatures, from hot wall to pack and from pot to pot. Air is not involved in radiation which spreads out in straight lines like light rays.

C. *Conduction*. Heat is transferred through all materials in kiln walls and pack and by contact from shelf to pot and from one wall layer to another.

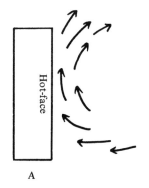

A

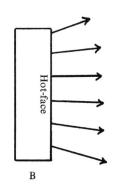

B

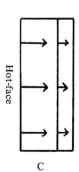

C

The law of cooling as proposed by Newton is that the rate of heat loss is proportional to the excess of temperature above the ambience. For your purposes this means the excess of the hot-face (surface of chamber wall) temperature over the cold-face (outside surface temperature of the kiln).

The rate of heat transfer or conductivity of materials such as brickwork and other compounds used in kiln walls and furniture is described in terms of thermal conductivity units. These may be measured as Btu per inch thickness per square foot of surface per hour per degree Fahrenheit, written as Btu in/ft^2 h $^\circ$F); in Watts/m$^\circ$C, or its international (SI) equivalent–joule m/m^{2}s$^\circ$C; or in other units. There is little standardization with suppliers and other references as to the units used. In any case it is the *comparative* figures within one scale which reveal the differing characteristics of a group of materials (see Table 4 p. 32). The higher the figure the more rapid the conductivity–in practice, the greater the heat loss from the chamber to the outer face. The figure will rise as the temperature in the kiln rises.

To give some examples from Moler's list of Insulating Refractories:

Moler Porous/34	1.31	units Btu in/ft^2 h $^\circ$F
MPK 23/42	1.45	at a mean (average)
MPK 26/48	2.36	temperature of
MPK 33/80	6.6	650/1200°T

The second figure (after the oblique line) indicates density in pounds per cubic foot. A more immediate understanding of heat conductivity can be derived from Diagram 15, which is sometimes used to indicate insulation properties.

Diagram 16 indicates a fairly dense brick with a high level of conductivity backed by an insulating material with a much lower rate. The backing would need to be chosen to stand the interface temperature of 980/1800°T. An extension of this to include intermediate figures is shown in Diagram 17. The insulation which is adequate for firing to 1050/1920°T can result in a dangerously hot outer face if used for stoneware at 1300/2370°T. The effectiveness of the insulation will always decrease as the difference between chamber and ambient temperature increases. It can also be seen that if a denser brick is used for the hot-face then the backing must be able to take a higher face temperature. The thickness of the insulator will, of course, influence the insulation it affords. There is also a time factor which bears upon Diagram 17, which is essentially that of the equilibrium state of the wall. In practice there is considerable delay in the response of the cold-face to the increasing hot-face temperature, due to heat storage and other factors, and a reasonably fast firing of seven to eleven hours would be over and the power switched off before the full cold-face temperature was reached. Under these conditions the cold-face temperatures can probably be reduced by one-third or even halved.

The temperature gradient in Diagrams 15, 16, and 17 is given as a straight line. It is now believed that, at temperatures above 1000/1830°T in a ceramic material, heat begins to flow more rapidly as the temperature rises. This may be due to the formation of glassy substances (which are thermal and electrical conductors in the molten state) within the brick. The result is that the gradient becomes curved.

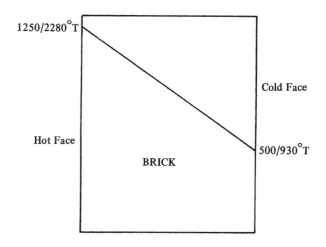

Diag. 15. The sloping line traces the temperature difference between hot- and cold-faces of brick or other material and indicates probable temperatures at intermediate points. The heat does not, of course, penetrate instantly and this type of diagram is often based on the maintenance of the hot-face at top temperatures for a given number of hours.

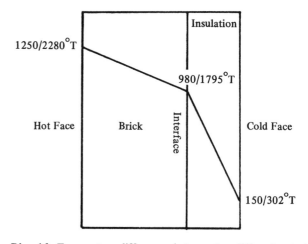

Diag. 16. Temperature differences between two different materials.

See Diagram 18. This would begin to have serious significance for potters only at 1300/2370°T and upwards. This includes SiC kilns which can attain 1400/2550°T. It must also be remembered that the elements are near 1350/2460°T if the chamber of a wire coil kiln is taken to 1290/2355°T. The most important consideration at high temperatures is that of the interface: it may be necessary either to increase the thickness of the hot-face brick, or to choose a backing insulation with greater heat tolerance. A half-inch of Fiberslab would be useful.

Heat storage, or absorption, will increase with density: more energy is needed to raise its temperature. The storage rate is expressed in Btu, calories, or joules, all indicating the quantity of heat required to raise the temperature of a unit mass of a substance one degree. Thus a firebrick with a rating (known as 'specific heat') of 30,000 Btu per square foot 9 inch thick can be compared to an insulating brick which takes around 7,000 Btu. The former needs four times the energy applied to it to raise its temperature by the same amount. The higher the specific heat figure, the more energy is needed to heat it.

The type of diagram shown in Diagrams 15, 16, and 17, is based on a given period of time that the hot-face is subjected to the temperature. As the whole brick becomes hotter its storage capacity decreases and, theoretically, the whole brick would attain an even temperature. With one face exposed this state is never achieved since the open face is radiating heat at an increasing rate as the temperature rises. An equilibrium is reached when the energy radiated is equal to that being expended in the chamber. At this point, which could be reached in practice in a poorly insulated or underpowered kiln, the chamber temperature would cease to increase. Similarly a very slow firing, by 'saturating' the brickwork and thus increasing the temperature of the cold-face, may result in a very slow rate of climb at the top range of temperature.

The walls of a kiln should therefore minimize both the conduction and storage of heat and this is attained by means of low density materials. Gases are obviously of low density, and a conveniently available gas is air. When enclosed in pores or pockets within a refractory material, it will greatly decrease both storage and heat conductivity

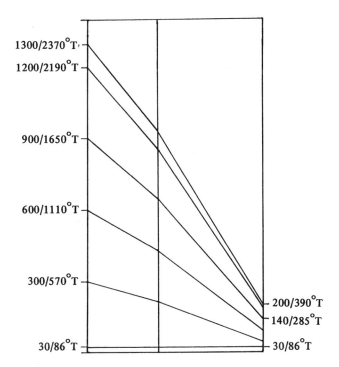

Diag. 17. Conduction showing intermediate temperatures.

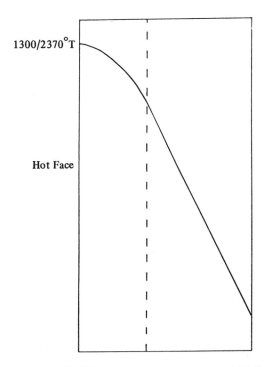

Diag. 18. Effect of conduction above 1000/1830°T.

31

figures. Insulating bricks and other compounds will thus have a spongelike texture, being permeated with air bubbles, either physically or chemically, during manufacture. The more open the texture the more efficient the insulation but, equally true, the weaker will be the physical structure of the material.

A balance must, therefore, always be struck between strength and insulation: the hot-face being constructed of a harder grade, the backing having maximum insulation value with consequent weaker structure.

It is possible, by means of fairly elaborate tables and precise information on the characteristics of the materials used, to work out the heat flow, the consequent loss from the chamber at different temperatures, and from these figures to arrive at the optimum power requirement in the kiln.

In *Calibrating* and *Calculating the Electric Kiln* M. Wikey details a method of arriving at the power needed to fire a kiln to a given temperature. Briefly his thesis rests upon an equation which involves wall thickness, conductivity figures, and the hot-face temperature required.

$$\frac{\text{hot-face temperature} \times \text{conductivity figure}}{\text{wall thickness (in inches)}}$$

$$\times \text{ mean area of kiln wall in ft}^2 =$$

power needed to fire kiln to a given temperature, in Btu per hour. To find power: watts = Btu/hr × 0.293

To arrive at practical figures to use in the equation:

1. Hot-face temperature must be expressed in °F.

2. Conductivity figures (which must be values of Btu in/ft²hr°F) are usually given for mean temperature. To arrive at the mean add together the figures for hot- and cold-faces of the wall and divide by two. Cold-face temperature is not one which is easily available. A few suppliers' lists provide them. An indication will be found on p. 34 in Graph 3.

TABLE 4
Comparative Conduction for Mean Temperatures in Btu in/ft² hr

	205/400°T	425/800°T	650/1200°T	870/1660°T	1100/2000°T
Firebrick	6.9	7.8	8.7	9.6	10.5
H.T. insulating K26/48	2.02	2.18	2.36	2.56	2.79
H.T. insulating K25/44	1.44	1.55	1.71	1.94	2.24
H.T. insulating K20/26	1.08	1.26	1.48	1.77	
Caposil	0.46	0.62	0.8		
ceramic fiber	0.32	0.6	0.76	1.4	1.82

EXAMPLE 1.

hot-face required	2340 (1280°C)
cold-face (as in Graph 3)	460
mean temperature	$= 2800 \div 2 = 1400$

3. Wall thickness. This can be taken as total thickness or effective thickness from the back of the element slot. Either will be a close approximation.

4. The mean area is arrived at by adding the total interior area to the total exterior area and dividing by two.

EXAMPLE 2.

A kiln chamber 2 ft × 2 ft × 2 ft with 3 in thick walls:

interior $2 \times 2 \times 6$	$= 24$ ft²
exterior $2.5 \times 2.5 \times 6$	$= 37.5$ ft²
mean area in ft²	$= 61.5 + 2 = 30.75$

EXAMPLE 3.

Using the figures mentioned above and checking the conductivity figure for 1400°F in Moler's catalog for K25/54 brick as 2.35 (See Table 16):

$$\frac{2340 \times 2.35}{3} \times 30.75 = 56,365 \text{ Btu}$$

$56,365 \times 0.293 = 16.515 \text{ kW}.$

This indicates that 16,515 watts are needed to bring an 8 ft³ kiln with 3 in K25/54 walls up to 1280/2340°T. It would then have a cold-face of 240/460°T—dangerously hot!

If insulation in the form of mineral-wool slab or similar material is added to lower the exterior temperature, Mr. Wikey suggests that each figure (for brick and insulation) be worked out separately, added together, and divided by two.

EXAMPLE 4.

Consider a kiln with 3 inches of brick as in Example 3 above, backed with 1 inch Caposil HTI.

The first problem is the interface which will represent the hot-face of the Caposil. Graph 3 on P. 34 gives approximate interface temperatures between 3 inches of brick and 1 inch

insulation. At 2340°F in the kiln the Caposil hot-face would be at around 646/1180°T. From Caposil's data sheet this gives a cold-face of 40/104°T. Repeating as for brick:

Hot-face 1180.

Conductivity at mean of $\frac{1180 + 104}{2} = 642°F$ is 0.56

Thickness 1 in

Mean area:	
$2.5 \times 2.5 \times 6 =$	37.5
$2.62 \times 2.62 \times 6 =$	41.2
	$78.7 \div 2 = 39.35$ ft²

$$\frac{1180 \times 0.56}{1} \times 39.35 = 26,100 \times 0.293 = 7,648 \text{ watts}$$

We now have the figure of 7,648 for the Caposil and 16,515 for the brick (Example 3) so:

$$\frac{7648 + 16515}{2} = 12082 \text{ watts of power would be needed for}$$

the combined layers of 3 in brick and 1 in Caposil.

EXAMPLE 5.

Using the equation for a 6 inch K26 wall as used by a number of commercial kiln builders:

$$\frac{2340 \times 2.55}{6} \times 39 = 38785 \times 0.293 = 11364 \text{ watts.}$$

Both figures seem a bit low for an 8 ft³ kiln but it must be remembered that they are for an empty kiln. If allowance is made for heat absorption by the pack and a little extra to cope with voltage drop, etc. the final figure is nearer to those given on p. 43 in Graph 5, where the U.K. average for an 8 ft³ commercial kiln is 18 KW and for the U.S. about 13 kW.

Figures arrived at in this way refer to straight firing with the kiln on full all the time. If gradations of input are effected by controls to slow down the rate of temperature increase, the cold-face will get warmer and this alters the calculations. More power will be needed to reach the same top temperature. The method can therefore be considered as an accurate guide to the minimum requirements of power.

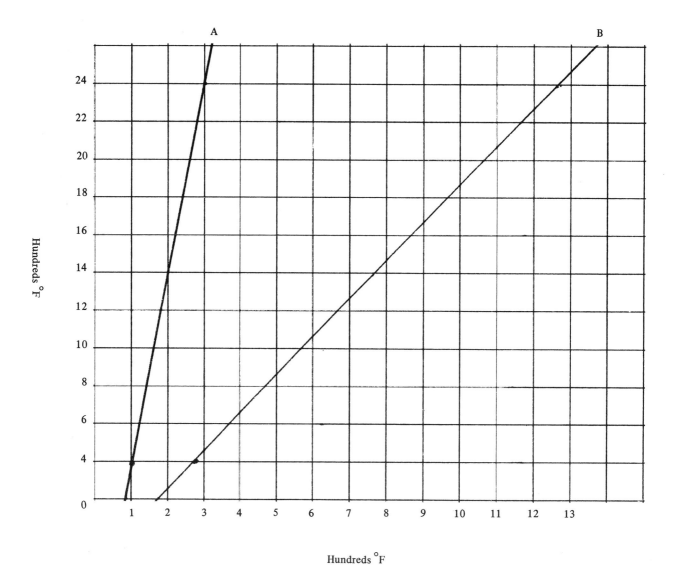

Graph 3. Graph showing the face temperature-relationships of a
2.5/63 mm K26 brick backed with "Supertemp" insulating slab. To
use the graph read across from line A to find hot-face temperatures,
and downwards for cold face. Read downwards from line B for interface temperatures. (Reproduced by kind permission M. Wikey).

FACTORS CONTROLLING HEAT LOSS

1. However efficient the insulation of kiln walls may be, the heat loss from the chamber will *increase in direct proportion to the surface area* of the hot-faces. Thus a wall 4 feet by 4 feet will lose four times as much heat as one 2 feet by 2 feet. It follows that the ratio will not be the same for volume as for wall area.

EXAMPLE 6.

A 1 ft^3 chamber has a wall area of 6 ft^2 (six faces including floor and roof) and a volume of 1 cubic foot: ratio 6:1.

A cube with 2 ft sides has a total wall area of $2 \times 2 \times 6 = 24$ ft^2, and a volume of $2 \times 2 \times 2 = 8$ ft^3: ratio 24:8, or 3:1. The heat loss, therefore, *decreases in relation to capacity the larger the kiln.*

2. Another factor, arising from the proposition above, which affects heat loss, is the shape of the chamber. As shown, a 2-foot-sided cube has a volume of 8 ft^3 and a wall area of 24 ft^2. Another chamber measuring $4 \times 2 \times 1$ has a similar volume but a wall area of 28 ft^2. The wall area of the second shape is 15 percent greater than that of the cube. In fact *any variation from the cube will increase the wall area and thus the heat loss.*

3. As discussed previously, heat loss will *increase as the difference between the ambient* (surrounding) *air temperature and that in the kiln chamber increases.*

4. The nearer a brick approaches to its full heat capacity, the hotter the outer face will become and the more heat will flow through the brick. *A long, slow rise in temperature is* therefore *more wasteful of energy than a shorter,* *quicker one.* After a certain amount of time the heat loss will come into virtual balance with input and the chamber will get no hotter—although the studio will! SiC rods have an advantage here—no lingering at 1250/2280-1350/2460°T.

5. A high heat capacity (specific heat figure) will mean that, although the exterior of the kiln may remain cool, energy is being invisibly consumed within the kiln doing work which may be of no direct value in the firing of the pots. *Low specific heat values are therefore to be aimed at* in order to save electricity in the heating of the kiln. A very low heat absorption figure will, however, affect the cooling rate. The mass of brickwork must release the stored heat and this can occur only through its thickness to the outer air. Materials with a very low specific heat such as ceramic fibers may result in a fast temperature rise with less fuel, but their insulating power may not be sufficient to prevent the stored heat in the ware from being dissipated rapidly through cold-face convection and radiation which will be similar in each case with corresponding fast cooling. A thick wall (6/150mm, or so) or ceramic fiber and mineral-wool block should have sufficient insulating quality to hold the heat within the chamber but would be initially expensive. In days of fast-rising electrical costs this may be balanced out in time. Perhaps the ideal solution is a combination of brick and low-heat-capacity slab. Your ware may not respond in a satisfactory manner to a fast rise and fall in temperature. In any case, glazes will show a different, though not necessarily inferior, color and quality to those from an all-brick kiln with a 40-hour or more cold-to-cold cycle.

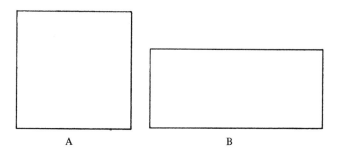

Diag. 19. The areas of the square and the rectangle are similar but the total length of sides are not. If A measures 3 m × 3 m the area is 9 m^2 and the perimeter measures, 4 × 3 m = 12 m. If B measures 2 m × 4.5 m = 9 m^2 area its perimeter measures (2 × 2 m) + (2 × 4.5 m) = 13 m.

TABLE 5
Approximate Comparative Heat Storage in Btu, ft^2

dense firebrick	30,000	⎫
H.T. insulating K26	8,000	⎬ 9/229 mm thick
H.T. insulating K24	6,000	⎭
Caposil	1,150	350 3/76 mm thick
ceramic fiber	1,650	280 1½/38 mm thick

Factors 3, 4, and 5 above obviously become more marked in their effect the higher the temperature in the chamber. This leads to a progressive slowing down in the rate of climb. A graph plotting the time/temperature will always give a curve resembling the trajectory of a rocket! Potters are familiar with the reluctance of kilns to achieve those last few degrees. Kiln B in Graph 6 on p. 45 can just attain 1040/1905°T; kiln A will never exceed 1250/2280°T. In fact kiln A and B are the same kiln, initially insufficiently powered.

Heat can be lost through poor design. Often this occurs at the door or lid: Loose or uneven brickwork can cause heat dissipation if the gaps are open to the outer air. Badly levelled top bricks in top-loaders, or ill-fitting doors are common causes of heat loss. Needless to say, cracks through walls can set up convection cooling, the more dangerous for being localized. An asbestos casing will minimize these effects. Any ventilation holes must be closed during the latter part of the firing. If there are upper and lower door spyholes, never open both at the same time.

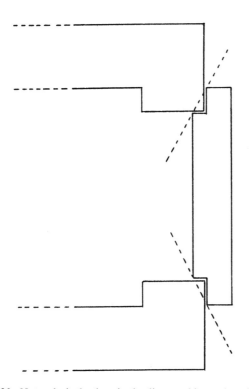

Diag. 20. Not only is the door in the diagram thinner than the walls but the dotted-line sections are narrower still. These proportions are, however, not infrequently found in kilns, both front- and top-loading.

HOT-FACE MATERIALS

The inside surface of the kiln must, obviously, be able to withstand the maximum temperature to which it may be subjected—and this includes the *element temperature* of some 50/80°T above that of the firing chamber. It must also bear the rapid rise and fall in temperature. The various grades of lightweight brick vary in constitution (higher alumina content for higher temperatures) and in density. From two to four density grades are available within each temperature grade. The density in Moler's list is indicated by a number which corresponds to its weight in kilograms per cubic meter. The density value tends to rise with the temperature rating.

The brickwork in an electric kiln is not subject to the degree of stress, physical abrasion, and gaseous attack which may operate in a fuel-burning kiln. Brick values very close to those operating in the chamber can be adequate, e.g., a K25 brick can be used for element temperatures up to 1350/2460°T. Above K25 prices rise steeply.

Lightweight H.T. (high temperature) bricks are given a prefix which indicates the working temperature they will stand without deformation. In England this is usually the letter K followed by a number; in the U.S. the letter K may be replaced with letters indicating the title of the manufacturer. The figures following the letter represent hundreds of degrees Fahrenheit, e.g., K23 can be used up to 2300°F (1260°C). Thus:

working temperatures of:	are serviceable up to:
K28	1540/2800°T
K26	1425/2600°T
K25	1370/2500°T
K23	1260/2300°T
K20	1095/2000°T

As mentioned, a brick may be given a second figure indicating kg/m^3. The most frequently used brick in electric kilns, K25, is listed by Moler Products in two densities: K25/44 and K25/54, with comparable thermal conductivity figures of 1.94 and 2.5 at 870/1600° mean temperature. The K25 brick contains around 41-percent alumina; the full range from K18 at 24-percent to K34 at 99-percent alumina. Brick K25/54 will offer a longer life where element slots are to be cut.

In any case it is advisable to check that the brick conforms to the following: iron oxide content below 1.5 percent, alkali content below 2 percent. Lower figures than these are quoted in *The Kiln Box* by Fred Olsen—1-percent iron and 0.4-percent alkali. Neither Gibbons Ltd. nor Moler bricks comply with the stricter standard but they have proved satisfactory in practice. Johns-Manville has a very good specification of 0.8-percent Fe_2O_3 and 0.1-percent alkali in their JM26 grade of H.T. insulating brick.

Lighweight refractory bricks are made in a standard size— 9 × 4½ × 3/229 × 114 × 76 mm—known, confusingly, as a 'straight' in the U.S. and a 'square' in the U.K. Other shapes are made for special purposes. It is possible to cut your own shapes from the commercially made 'straights' but it may be economical, if time is valuable, to buy, for instance, arch bricks where needed. Some of the most useful prepared shapes are illustrated in Diagram 21. Cutting bricks is discussed in Chapter 5.

Ceramic fiber can also be used at the hot-face and manufacturers now offer a cast panel with element slots already formed. The fiber is made by blowing high velocity gas jets onto a molten stream of high-purity aluminum silicate. The stream is blown into fluffy, white, cottonlike fibers which can be exposed to high temperatures without alteration: 1260/2300°T for ordinary grades but up to 1400/2550°T for special high qualities. Longer threads are produced by spinning.

Kilns have been built in which the wire element is wound round silica rods supported by short slots in brick pillars, the intermediate spaces being lined with ceramic fiber felt (such as Carborundum's Fiberfrax) held in place with ceramic pins which are anchored to the outer skin of Sindanyo asbestos. Between the ceramic fiber and asbestos sheet is a 2½/64mm layer of calcium silicate insulation such as Caposil.

The necessity for silica rods makes this system difficult for studio potters to imitate. Silicon-carbide rods in place of wire coils could, however, be used very effectively and need no intermediate support. The result would be a very lightweight kiln.

Ill. 5. Ceramic wool or "blanket."

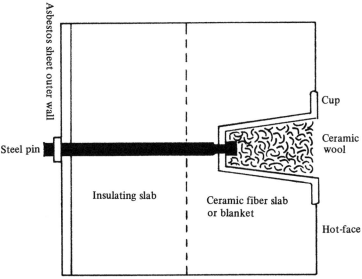

Diag. 22. The (black) metal pins hold a ceramic "cup" with a flanged rim which is pressed into the fiber and tightened by means of a nut on the outside of the kiln wall. The end of the pin is protected from the full heat of the hot-face by a stuffing of ceramic wool.

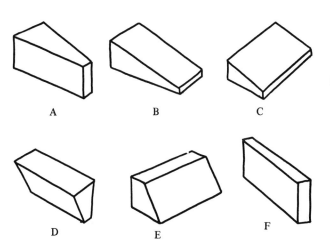

Diag. 21. Some manufactured brick shapes: A. End Arch, B. Feather end or Scewback, C. Feather side, D. Side Arch, E. Springer block, F. Split.

The preformed element holders mentioned earlier, if used above earthenware temperatures, must be made in high-quality material such as Fiberfrax H. Panels are made up to 2/0.62 mm by 3/0.93 m in size. Ceramic fiber in any form is rather easily damaged. The panels and slabs have a texture similar to that of expanded polystyrene tiles. They are also subject to vitrification, as is to be expected from a ceramic material. This increases friability. It is a continuing process which begins at around 1150/2100°T for the lower grades and from 1375/2500°T in the best 62-percent alumina grade. Shrinkage will therefore be lower in the better fibers. 'Saffil', a fiber by Imperial Chemical Industries Ltd. (I.C.I.) will stand 1600/2900°T.

Slabs or felt can be pinned into place as shown in Diagram 22 or can be glued to the backing with special adhesive such as Fiberfix, though this is not recommended by the manufacturers at working temperatures much above 1200/2200°T.

The doubtful qualities of ceramic fiber (apart from relatively high cost), especially at the hot-face, concern its physical strength; its apparently decreasing insulation value at top temperatures compared to brick; and its low heat storage which, while it will save fuel, will also involve rapid rates of heating and cooling which may not suit a pottery body or glaze.

It is likely, however, that improved technology will overcome the main disadvantages of friability and comparatively high cost in which case the undoubted advantages of ceramic fiber in weight and fuel saving compared with brick may lead to something of a revolution in kiln design. As previously mentioned it can be used very effectively with SiC rods, its low physical strength being much less of a drawback when coils do not have to be supported.

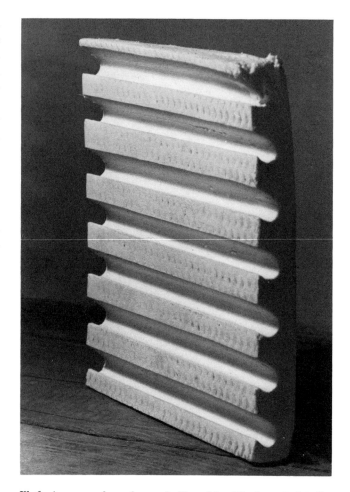

Ill. 6. A vacuum-formed ceramic-fiber slab with element slots (by Carborundum Ltd). Evidence of its friability can be seen at the top front corner which was damaged in transit and has continued to break away. Although only about 1 inch thick behind the slots, it is claimed that the insulation gives a 300/570°T drop between the hot-face and the outer cold-face.

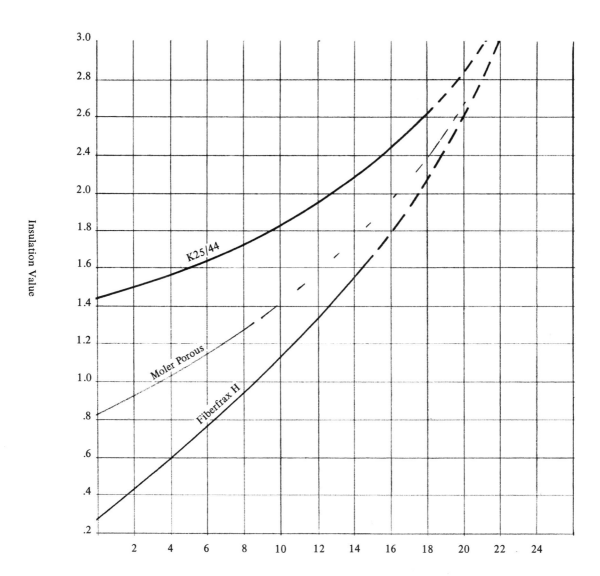

Graph 4. Comparative insulation values of three types of kiln-wall material. The dotted lines extrapolate the curves derived from published figures (solid lines). Moler Porous would not, of course, endure temperatures of over 1000°C and the line has been suggested for comparison only. It will be seen that the insulation figures approach much closer at elevated temperatures.

BACKING MATERIALS (INSULATORS)

For the outer lining of kiln walls, where the temperature will not normally exceed 950/1730°T, the range of possible materials is much wider than for the hot-face.

The H.T. type brick already discussed can be used in its lower grades—K16 to K20 according to the interface temperature—as can other types of bricks, slabs, blocks, and loose fillings. These include the following.

DIATOMACEOUS RED SLABS

Maximum temperature about 850/1550°T. These are rather dusty red 'squares' or 12 × 12 × 3/310 × 310 × 75mm blocks, often imperfectly squared up and sometimes slightly warped. They are very good insulators—1.31 Btu conductivity at 650/1200°T. Made by Moler.

MINERAL WOOL BLOCKS

Maximum temperature about 1000/1830°T (varies). These are sold under various trade names including Caposil, Kipsulate, Nutherm, PV Supertemp, etc. They are now asbestos-free calcium-silicate materials. Although very light, friable, and dusty to cut and use, once sandwiched between the inner brickwork and a Transite (Asbestolux in the U.K.) or metal outer skin, they should come to no harm. They will replace twice their thickness of insulation brick, and can be cut with a saw or knife. Use a mask when handling. Shrinkage is about 2 percent at 1000/1830°T and the blocks will show cracks in the surface if held rigid while heating. There are adhesives available. They are excellent insulators— 0.72 at 500/930°T. Sizes:

Kipsulate (Moler)	Two grades 950/1750 and 1000/1850°T	All 1/25 mm to 4/100 mm thick
	36 × 6/915 × 150 mm	
	36 × 12/915/305 mm	
	36 × 24/915 × 610 mm	
Caposil	Standard size 36 × 24/915 × 610 but also 12/305 mm wide	Thicknesses as Kipsulate

Supplied by Moler, Babcock and Wilcox, Cape Insulation, Eagle-Pitcher, etc.

MICROPORE

Maximum Temperature 950/1740°T. This is a sophisticated and superefficient insulator which needs very careful handling since its effectiveness is destroyed if a slab is broken or cracked. It must therefore be well protected from local pressure or strain. Sizes are made to order at the factory and it is supplied in a bag or envelope which is re-tained during fitting and disintegrates under the effect of heat. A firm, outer skin and well-fitting, and preferably cemented, brickwork are essential, as is a rigid frame. Under perfect conditions $\frac{1}{2}$/13 mm of Micropore can replace 3/75 mm of insulating brick. It is obtainable through Labheat of Ironbridge, and is now made with a facing of ceramic fiber which greatly extends its possibilities.

CERAMIC FIBER (wool, blanket, felt, board, etc.)

Maximum, temperature 1250/2280 to 1600/2900. This material has been described under Hot-Face Materials. It has little advantage over mineral-wool as a backing insulator and its price is considerably higher. Its very low heat storage can save fuel and the material is very light in weight, but this is also true of other insulators. If a thin brick is used at the hot-face with consequently high interface temperature, it could be backed with 1/25 mm of fiber followed by mineral-wool block. The cheaper Fiberslab from Carborundum will stand full hot-face heat and can be used to back the thinnest brick.

The types and sizes of fiber available are too numerous to mention fully. The slab, blanket, and felt forms are the most useful; most them are available $\frac{1}{4}$/6 mm to 1/25 mm thick in 12/305, 24/610, and 4/1220 mm wide rolls, 25/7.625 m long. There is also a castable fiber. Manufacturers: Carborundum, Morgans, I.C.I. Johns-Manville; and also supplied by Superamics.

ALUMINA BUBBLES

Maximum temperature according to quality around 1500/2730°T. These are little hollow bubbles of alumina (aluminum oxide). Grade 4 is available, maximum diameter about 5 mm. It can be used as a loose fill or cast with refractory cement. Supplied by Carborundum.

ALUMINUM FOIL

Melts at 650/1200°T. Foil insulates by the reflection of heat rather than by impeding its permeation. It is only effective, therefore, as long as it is bright and shiny. Some improvement of performance can be obtained by introducing a sheet of foil between the outer insulation and the skin of the kiln.

The *danger*, in an electric kiln is that *of possible contact or short circuit* between element tails and foil. It must be positioned carefully to avoid this hazard. Sizes: rolls 1/0.31 m-2/0.62 m wide.

VERMICULITE

Maximum temperature 900/1650°T. This is an expanded

mica for backing insulation fill, or as a mortar aggregate. It is crushable, and must be protected. It can be poured into a cavity or mixed with aluminous cement and cast as required. There are various makers. (It is used for house insulation, etc).

ASBESTOS SHEET

Disintegrates over 500/930°T. In recent years there has been a good deal of concern over the use of asbestos, which is a naturally occurring silicate of magnesium and calcium. The lung disease asbestosis can be contracted by inhaling even small amounts of fiber. When cutting or filing any asbestos compound, it is essential to wear a mask, which can be of the simple cloth-filter type. Once in position and used with common sense, asbestos sheet should not pose any great danger. Types available are:

Asbestos cement. A hard, brittle board which warps and splits under heat and is not recommended. Transite asbestos cement is, however, adequate for the cladding of a well-insulated kiln.

Asbetolux. (Trade name) A steam-pressed asbestos sheet which will endure considerable warmth and pressure if properly fitted. It is used for the outer skin only. It can be cut with a saw—but wear a mask, even when sweeping up afterwards. Sheet size 8/2.44m by 4/1.22m and from $\frac{1}{8}$/ 3 mm to 1/25 thick. Johns-Manville also makes a steam-pressed asbestos.

Wood asbestos. A cross-ply material with greater cracking resistance (though softer) than Asbestolux. Same sizes as Asbestolux. Useful thickness for kilns is $\frac{3}{8}$/9mm.

Sindanyo. (Trade name) A very hard material which needs to be cut professionally by machine. It is especially useful for connector panels, but too expensive for cladding.

REFRACTORY CEMENT

Maximum Temperature 900/1650–1400/2550°T according to type and aggregate. There are many makes of high-temperature mortars and high-alumina cements which can be mixed with a suitable aggregate such as vermiculite for low temperatures, crushed firebrick for higher temperatures but lower insulation qualities, and alumina bubbles for either end of the heat scale.

Mortars may be designed to set cold (often with the use of sodium silicate) when they are known as air-setting cements, or under the effects of heat, heat-set, or both. Ciment Fondu has a maximum of around 1350/2460°T; others such as Moler, Steetley, etc., vary from 1000/1830°T to 1700/3000°T. The heat resistance rises with alumina

content. Slabs or more complicated shapes can be cast in refractory cement by the usual casting methods, or outer walls of kilns can be cast in situ.

Ill. 7. Ceramic fiber felt, blanket, string, paper, etc. (Photo reproduced by kind permission of Carborundum Company Ltd.)

Ill. 8. Alumina bubbles.

5. Design and Construction of the Kiln Box

GENERAL CONSIDERATIONS

Avoid complication and too great a degree of permanence, at least in your first kiln. A simple, dry-built design can be more versatile in the sense that it can be altered, mistakes put right, and parts re-used in future kilns. Although H.T. insulating bricks are relatively soft compared with firebrick they will, with care, last indefinitely and can be used in successive kilns. Casting the outer insulation will give a strong, rigid structure but will also render it monolithic and virtually incapable of alteration if it does not turn out to be wholly successful.

There are a number of aspects to be considered and decided upon before getting down to working out the kiln in detail.

1. The *maximum temperature* at which you wish to operate. As indicated in Chapter 4 this will affect all other factors: type and thickness of insulation, type and loading of elements, amount of power needed, etc.

2. The *size* of the packing space. By careful planning of your output you can get 100 or more pieces into a 7 ft^3 kiln. A larger kiln may be essential for sculptural or big handbuilt ware, of course, but in my experience two smaller kilns are more versatile for tableware, using one fired kiln for drying pots and both for keeping the workshop itself warm. In any case the size may be controlled by your elec-

trical supply (but not the number of kilns, see Chapter 7).

3. The *amount of current* you can draw from an existing or proposed supply. If, for instance, after consultation with your electric company, they say that 15 kW is the maximum power available without incurring expenses which you feel would be uneconomical, then your muffle size is limited to about 7 ft^3 for stonewares and 9 ft^3 for earthenware firings. If you can get a three-phase supply this will usually allow for as much consumption as you are likely to require. Graph 5, which is derived from figures quoted in kiln manufacturers' brochures, may serve as a guide to power requirements. There is a marked disparity between them which may be explained by the very fast heating and cooling rates of the U.S. kilns which have thinner walls and consequently lower heat storage. The outside of these kilns must get very hot if the firing is prolonged. The limits of the graphs are 1–40 ft^3, the average potter's range.

An analysis of the U.K. curve shows that the extra power needed for a unit increase in volume is steadily reduced as the kiln size increases. See Chapter 4.

It follows from Table 6 that a pot which costs $.20 (10p in the U.K.) to fire in a 40 ft^3 electric kiln would cost $1 (50p in the U.K.) in a 1 ft^3 kiln if we consider consumption alone and assume that the same rate per unit were charged for both kilns.

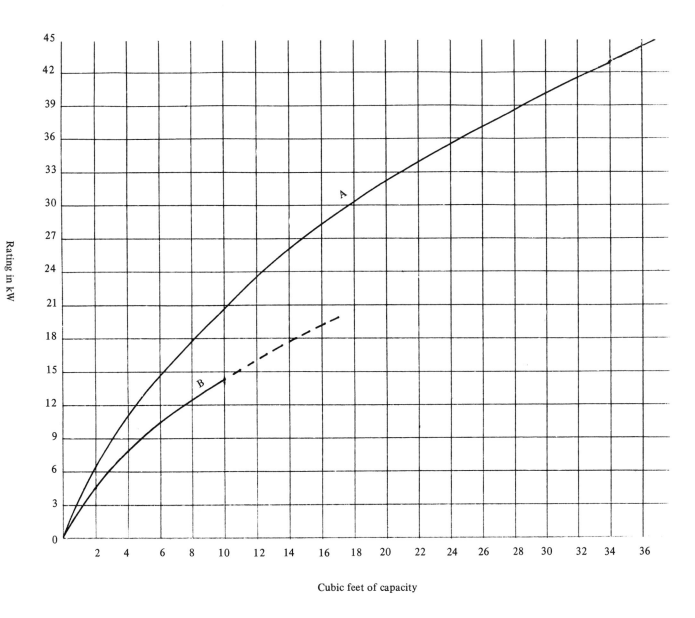

Graph 5. Power/chamber-volume relationships in commercial kilns
in U.K. (A) and U.S. (B). (Reproduced by permission of Russell
Davis and Ceramic Review).

If the volume is too great for the power, the equilibrium state beyond which the temperature in the chamber will show no further significant increase with time, may be lower than the desired firing temperature. There is, for instance, a 13/330 mm cube kiln on the British market which is powered by less than 3 kW (it can be plugged into a 13 amp socket) but which takes 19 hours to reach 1240/2265°T.

TABLE 6
Power/Volume Relationship in British Commercial Kilns

Volume in Firing Chamber	kW Required	kW Increase per Cubic Foot
1 cubic foot	3.75	
2 cubic feet	6.50	2.75
3 cubic feet	9.00	2.50
4 cubic feet	11.00	2.00
5 cubic feet	13.00	2.00
6 cubic feet	14.50	1.50
8 cubic feet	17.50	1.50
10 cubic feet	20.50	1.50
15 cubic feet	27.00	1.30
30 cubic feet	40.00	0.90
40 cubic feet	48.00	0.80

TABLE 6A
Power/Volume Relationship in American Commercial Kilns

Volume of Firing Chamber	kW Required	kW Increase per Cubic Foot
1 cubic foot	3	
2 cubic feet	4.5	2.5
3 cubic feet	6.5	2.0
4 cubic feet	8.0	1.5
5 cubic feet	9.25	1.25
6 cubic feet	10.5	1.25
8 cubic feet	12.75	1.125
10 cubic feet	14.5	1.125

No figures for kilns over 10 ft³ have been made available to the author.

More efficient insulation with materials of low specific heat (heat storage) or better use of the resistance wire (see note to Graph 6) can help to push up the volume/power ratio. Graph 6 is derived from my experience in designing a kiln in which the power was strictly limited by the supply and the ratio was pushed too far. Curve A indicates the first pyrometer readings. There was virtual equilibrium at about 1050/1920°T. Curve B was achieved by shortening the circuit by 5 feet (thus increasing power input which was balanced by the fact of a voltage drop due to a long lead from the mains), and by replacing straight and hairpin elements with double hairpins thus putting about another 3 feet of useful wire into the kiln by saving it on the 'tails'! The probable equilibrium was raised to about 1220/2230°T.

All kilns will, of course, have an equilibrium point but this is often so high (1350/2460°T and over) that the ware and, more important, the kiln shelves and elements are destroyed before it is reached. It is possible to build a kiln with an equilibrium point of 1000/1830°T and lower as Graph 6 indicates. Equilibrium with SiC rods is always below element damage point.

4. The *shape of the packing space*. An oblong plan with length of sides in an approximate 2/3 ration proves convenient and economical in practice. This is not the most efficient shape from the firing point of view, since any variation from the cube increases heat loss, but there are always several aspects of efficiency to consider. Too great a depth in a front-loading kiln can make packing difficult. It is advisable that at least two facing banks of elements be within 30/760 mm, or at the most 3/0.9 m, of one another.

5. The *shape and size of available kiln shelves* may be a determining factor in your kiln plan. The range, which used to be very wide, is decreasing and you should enquire of suppliers what is available. A gap of between $\frac{1}{2}$/13mm and 1/25mm should be allowed between the shelf edge and the kiln wall to allow for some circulation of heat; to prevent the edge of the shelf getting too hot; and to allow for the width of your fingers when setting the shelf. Shelves can be cut to size with an abrasive disc on a power drill but the disc wears very quickly and a great deal of choking dust is produced. The disks are sometimes useful for cutting the roof batts for top-loaders. Wear a mask.

6. The *type of kiln*—front- or top-loader—will control the placing of the elements and the degree of engineering skill needed to frame and support the structure.

7. Design the kiln with available *refractory-brick sizes* in mind. A great deal of work can be avoided by using whole bricks and slabs. This will, in general, mean considering the chamber in multiples of $9 \times 4\frac{1}{2} \times 3$ in (230 × 115 ×

75 mm) for the hot-face (in U.S. 9 × 4½ × 2½) with outer insulation of 36/915 mm × 6/153 mm slabs for most makes of mineral-wool, though other sizes are also supplied.

8. A kiln, even if built of lightweight refractories will be quite heavy when finished and packed. An all-brick design might gross 1 cwt (50 kilos) per cubic foot of packing space. The floor must be capable of taking this weight plus a couple of potters thumping round it. A minor consideration but one which can affect performance is the temperature and draftiness of the kiln room. A badly insulated shed in winter can lengthen the firing time appreciably.

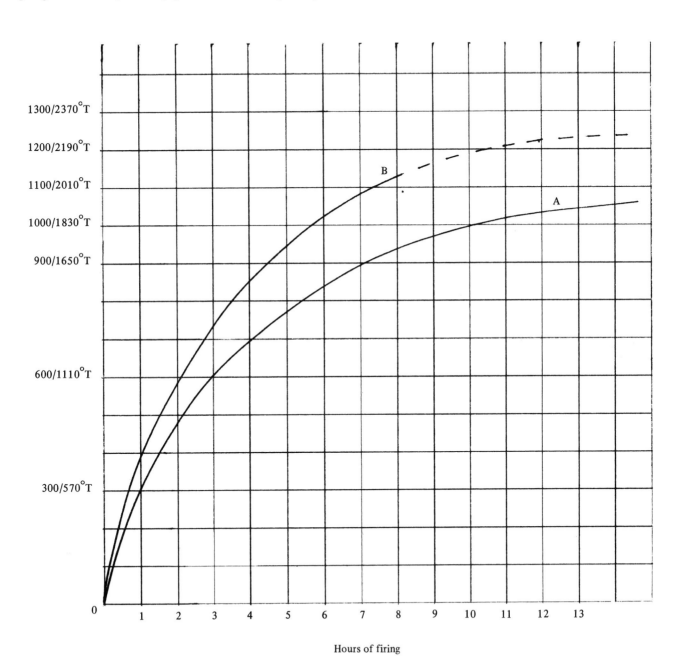

Graph 6. Kiln chamber 2.8 ft². Power 6-6.5 kW.

KILN BOX

A kiln consists of a skeleton framework, cladding or outer skin fastened onto or within the frame, a layer of insulating refractories, and finally the inner hot-face bricks. It is easier to assemble the various layers from the outside inwards but, in order to arrive at a tight fit within the framework, it is advisable to cut and mockup the brickwork and insulation so that it can be precisely measured for the frame.

Ill. 9. The hot-face bricks (18 × 4.5 × 9 inch slabs used here) assembled to check precise exterior size overall.

FRAME

The bricks are usually held in place by some sort of metal frame. If the bricks are mortared or a continuous insulating skin is cast in removable shuttering, then the frame can be reduced to a horizontal rectangle on short legs or brick piles. It is also possible to hold the corner angle in place by means of strapping or wire wound round the kiln. Normally, however, a complete angle-iron frame is constructed, either welded or bolted together, and the brickwork assembled within it. In rare cases the frame is built round the brickwork but this can prove difficult.

If you are very sure of your design and anticipate a long period with the same sized kiln, then a riveted or welded angle iron provides a frame free of the protuberances of bolts. As previously recommended, check the precise frame size by building a mock-up of the bricks, insulation, and cladding. Half an inch tight or loose can lead to a lot of extra work.

For the average builder some form of slotted angle is called for. Experimental kilns can then be built, altered, or dismantled with ease. The type with vertical and horizontal slots is the more versatile.

The size of angle will obviously depend on the weight of the kiln. As a guide:

$1\frac{1}{2}$/38 mm by $1\frac{1}{2}$/38 mm angle for kilns 2–5 ft^3 slotted
$1\frac{1}{2}$/38 by $2\frac{1}{2}$/63 mm angle for kilns 5–12 ft^3 slotted
2/50 × 2/50 × $\frac{3}{32}$/2.5 mm angle
    for kilns 5–10 ft^3 ⎫
                          ⎬ welded or rivetted
2/50 × 2/50 × $\frac{1}{8}$/3.5 mm angle
    for kilns 10–15 ft^3 ⎭

Ill. 10. Three fairly readily available types of slotted angle for framing bricks. The center angle is perhaps the most versatile.

Ill. 11. Where it is difficult to line up bolt holes for a tight fit round the brickwork, a corner can be connected with one of the triangular plates (supplied with most slotted angle kits) as shown here.

The kiln will need legs as well as a frame: 5/125 mm to 12/305 mm for top-loaders; 27/685 mm to 36/915 mm for front-opening styles. The former depend on the height of the kiln box which should have a top surface (without roof) not more than about 39/1000 mm high to allow for easy packing. A conveniently sited loading chamber for a front-loader will depend on your own height. Experiment with various surface heights. The legs are usually extensions of the corner angle-iron uprights, suitably steadied with cross-stays if longer than about 12 inches. The space beneath a front-loader, and extensions above it if it is not too high, can be slatted to receive shelves for storing and drying wares.

Provision for the housing and protection of the element connections must be considered at this stage. In a top-loader with continuous four-wall elements (see Diagram 57) this is situated at one corner only. For straight- and hairpin-wire elements in a top-loader the housing covers the full area at each end of the kiln. Front-loading kilns with elements in three walls and floor are connected at the back wall only. All these provisions are for coiled-wire elements. The depth of housing need be only $2\frac{1}{2}$/65 mm is asbestos cladding is used but 3/75 mm to 4/100 mm is necessary for metal cladding. The former is recommended for potter-builders as it is an insulating material.

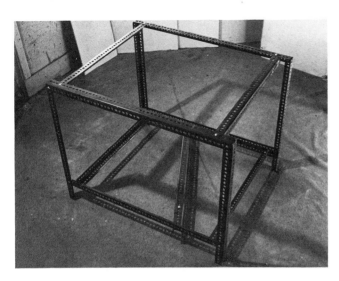

Ill. 12. A typical simple frame for top-loading kilns up to about 10/0.3 m³. The side members are extended 3/75 mm to form element connection panels.

Ill. 13. The asbestos sheet has been unbolted from the end of a top-loader to show element connections. The slotted angle allows plenty of ventilation, which is essential.

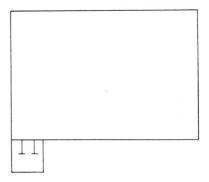

Diag. 23. Tail housing for element connections on top-loaders. With all-round four wall elements.

Diag. 24. End housings for straight and hairpin wire elements in top-loading kilns.

Diag. 25. Back-wall connection housing for front-loading kilns.

47

When using horizontal SiC rods, top-loaders will follow the plan of Diagram 24. The normal rod needs connections at each end and this poses some design problems with front-loaders.

In top-loading kilns using straight and hairpin elements or SiC rods, and for the rear connections of front-loaders, the horizontal angle-iron frame members can be continued 3 or 4 inches to allow for housing the element connections. See Illustration 13.

The floor area will need intermediate support to take the considerable weight of brick and pack. Sample arrangements of extra lengths of angle (with flat side uppermost of course) are illustrated in Diagram 27.

A typical front-loader kiln frame is shown diagrammatically in the specifications given for Kiln 3 in Chapter 10.

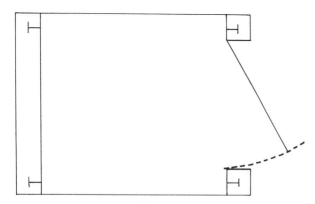

Diag. 26. Connection housing for front-loaders using horizontal S.C. rods.

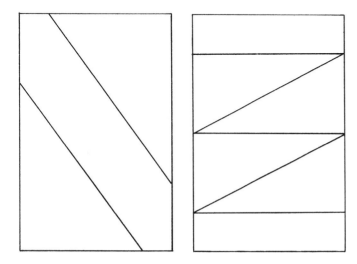

Diag. 27. Sample arrangements for floor-support angle iron.

CASING OR CLADDING

A kiln of mortared brick construction will not need an outer skin, though one may be added for neatness or to offer a smooth surface. Casing will also prevent drafts if cracks appear in the walls. For loose-built brick, or brick and slab, a containing box is obviously valuable, while for the more delicate insulators such as alumina bubbles, mineral-wool block, or ceramic fiber, a firm cladding is essential. If the insulation is to be cast in situ, then a tight casing can act as shuttering.

Metal or asbestos-based sheet is the most common cladding material. Metal has the advantage of strength and rigidity; asbestos is more effective as an additional insulator providing that the wall is thick enough to prevent it from getting too hot. One is not so likely to burn oneself on asbestos as on hot metal. If a sheet of shiny foil is introduced on the inside face of either material it will improve its performance. See Chapter 4 for the dangers and advantages of these materials. Metal cladding must be completely shielded from any possible contact with elements or other electrically 'live' connections. Metal can be bolted or welded onto the frame; asbestos may be bolted or simply held in place in the angle iron by the weight and pressure of the bricks and slabs. Suitable thicknesses are 18 swg (1.2 mm) for metal sheet and $\frac{3}{16}$/5 to $\frac{3}{8}$/10 mm for asbestos.

Ill. 14. Detail of frame illustrated in Ill. 12. The corner member allows a 0.5/12 mm or so gap to accommodate the sheet of Asbestolux or other cladding used. Note: the cladding will need to be cut or drilled to fit over the bolt at the corner of the frame, as must be done for all protruding belts in the construction.

Ill. 15. The frame previously shown has been furnished with asbestos sheet, and some of the outer insulating blocks are in place (Moler's red slabs are used here).

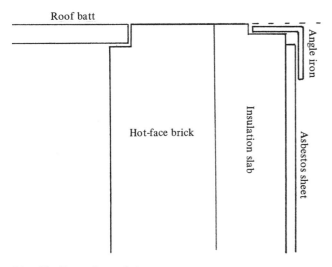

Diag. 28. Recess for angle iron.

Ill. 16. The outer skin is almost complete. The 12/305 mm square slabs could be replaced with Caposil or any of the other insulators listed.

A firm area must be provided at the base of the kiln. If it is to be a very permanent and heavy structure a plinth of Thermalite or similar blocks (not ordinary cast concrete) can be laid down. Generally, however, a kiln will be supported on bricks or metal legs, and the base is simply the sheet of metal or asbestos similar to the cladding which is laid within the angle iron. Provided the kiln is supported by one or more cross-lengths of angle (see previous section) then $\frac{1}{4}$/6 mm or $\frac{3}{8}$/10 mm asbestos will suffice for kilns up to 24/610 mm by 36/915 mm plan size.

INSULATION BRICKS AND SLABS

These are designed to hold as much heat within the kiln as possible. They are not subject to the full heat of the firing and can be of any refractory material which will stand 1000/1830°T. Since they consist as far as possible of trapped air pockets they can be very light in weight. Most of the weight-saving in a kiln, therefore, is concentrated here. Most of the types available are listed in Chapter 4. In most cases it will not be necessary to cement or fix them in place: they will be sandwiched tightly between the hot-face brick and cladding.

Loose insulators or those to be cast in situ need special treatment. The outer skin must be firmly fixed into the frame; the inner bricks should be cemented together and held in place by refractory brick spacers.

Unless you are very sure of your design I would not recommend casting the insulation since this renders the kiln virtually monolithic and hence unalterable—and nearly immovable!

If possible rebate the insulation bricks or blocks to make the metal angle flush with the top face of top-loaders. If the insulation is only the width of the angle, the hot-face bricks are set at the height of the metal surface. Some settlement always takes place so it might be a good idea to set the angle about 2 mm below the top level. This will make it easier to assemble the roof right across the top of the kiln.

The insulation should be such that, at the peak of the firing, the outside is not much hotter than the hand can touch.

HOT FACE

Hot-face bricks for electric kilns must be soft enough to saw, iron-free, and have a deformation rating at least 60/110°T above the proposed maximum chamber temperature. The various kinds available are listed in Chapter 4. They should also possess maximum insulation properties consistent with strength.

It is possible to buy hot-face slabs up to $9 \times 18 \times 4\frac{1}{2}/$ $229 \times 457 \times 114$ mm which can be used very advantageously in a dry-built kiln. It is cheaper to use standard bricks. In small kilns they can be set dry and, so long as they fit tightly, need no fixing. The corners can be keyed as shown in Diagrams 29A and 29B. In "A" the corner is cut back the whole width of the inset brick, in "B" there is less cutting of the joint but the gap must be filled with a third piece which may itself involve sawing. Alternatively, hoops of wire (element wire) preferably 13 swg can be inserted into the top faces of the bricks. With careful cutting and the use of a little cement, small fillets of kiln brick can replace the wire.

If bricks are to be mortared together, manufacturers advise that they be soaked in water before mortar is applied. If this is done, there is a danger that they will still be wet when current is first passed through the elements and shock can be experienced through the fabric of the kiln. Dry the bricks as completely as possible by other means before fitting the elements which can be damaged by excessive steam. It is possible, however, to thin the cement itself with water and to lay the bricks dry or after just a quick dunk in water. The mortar must be of the same refractory rating as the bricks, and as free from iron or alkalis. There are many varieties on the market for both air and heat setting (see Chapter 4). The cement is applied very thinly; 'buttered' is the expressive professional term. For large kilns, roof arches, etc., a mortar is obviously useful but for chambers up to 8–10 ft^3 pinning or slotting will usually suffice.

Larger kilns of 18/.5 m^3 and over may need expansion joints. The hot-face will expand under the influence of heat before the framework. The average allowance is only about $\frac{1}{16}$/1.5 mm per foot of wall. In a dry-built kiln there is generally enough 'give' in the construction. Expansion gaps can be located at the corners of the chamber and can be packed with ceramic wool.

Some arrangements of hot-face and insulating layers which have given good service are illustrated in Diagram 32A, B, C. I have not tested arrangements D and E but I am sure they would repay experiment.

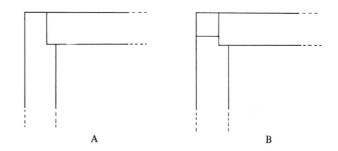

Diag. 29. Keyed corners.

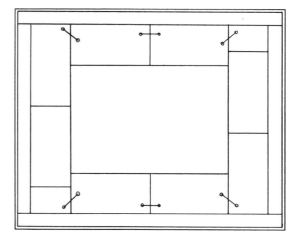

Diag. 30. A small top-loader plan (at any brick-face level of the walls) showing placing of wire hoops to hold brick in position.

Ill. 17. The walls can be held in place at the base by raising the floor, as shown here, either by using the base bricks on edge or by inserting thin slabs between the hot-face bricks and insulating layer.

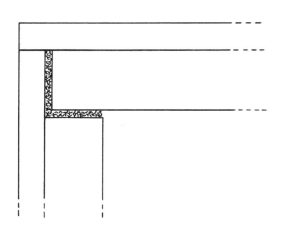

Diag. 31. Corner expansion joints. The spaces can be packed with ceramic wool.

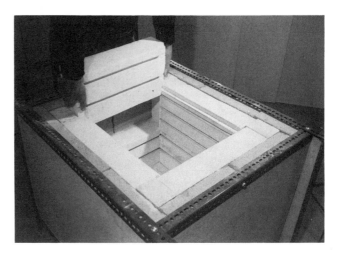

Ill. 18. The last slab is sliding (the same principle would apply to standard bricks). Keyed corners can be seen here. System B in Diagram 29 has been adopted here.

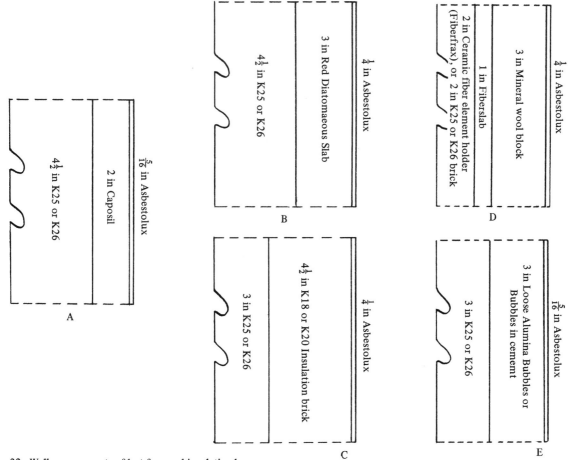

A
- $4\frac{1}{2}$ in K25 or K26
- 2 in Caposil
- $\frac{5}{16}$ in Asbestolux

B
- $4\frac{1}{2}$ in K25 or K26
- 3 in Red Diatomaeous Slab
- $\frac{1}{4}$ in Asbestolux

C
- 3 in K25 or K26
- $4\frac{1}{2}$ in K18 or K20 Insulation brick
- $\frac{1}{4}$ in Asbestolux

D
- 2 in Ceramic fiber element holder (Fiberfrax), or 2 in K25 or K26 brick
- 1 in Fiberslab
- 3 in Mineral wool block
- $\frac{1}{4}$ in Asbestolux

E
- 3 in K25 or K26
- 3 in Loose Alumina Bubbles or Bubbles in cement
- $\frac{5}{16}$ in Asbestolux

Diag. 32. Wall arrangements of hot-face and insulating layers.

ROOF

For all top-loader and upright kilns with a maximum plan size of about 24/610 mm by 15/380 mm, two kiln batts or shelves $\frac{3}{4}$/19 mm thick can be used, thinner for small kilns. Two shelves side by side offer a 'controlled crack' and lessen the possibility of dunting. Do not imagine, however, that they will be stronger if supported by a wide seating in the brick walls. This seating should be no more than $\frac{3}{4}$/19 mm wide or the temperature range over the batt will inevitably lead to dunting and probably a collapse of the roof. If these rules are followed, however, and good quality alumina batts are used, they will stand the strain almost indefinitely. If a curve develops the batt can be reversed. Small surface cracks from the edges will not hurt.

Above the slabs the brick must be of hot-face quality and at least 3/75 mm thick. If slabs can be obtained they will place less load on the batts than will bricks but the latter can be used. A second layer of insulator, as lightweight as possible, is finally covered with a sheet of Asbestolux or similar material. The assembly of bricks or slabs over the roof of top-loaders is so quick and easy that the provision of a heavy hinged lid is unnecessary. The lids provided on commercial kilns are usually too thin. The lid, like a door in an upright kiln, should be as efficient an insulator as the rest of the walls—if anything, more so. If one of the more friable insulation materials is used it will be necessary to provide a casing and this can be done as in Diagram 33. Their light weight makes it possible to lift the whole assembly from a small kiln without much effort. On a larger kiln (say, 36/915 mm by 40/1016 mm overall roof measurements) it may be necessary to hinge this part of the lid.

For smaller front-loaders a very lightweight roof composed of 1 inch of Fibreslab H quality (Carborundum) can be laid on the roof bats and covered with 2 inches of mineral wool slab and a sheet of Asbestolux.

A more professional roof can be arched. Arch bricks or alternate arch and standard can be used, or squares can be cut. For smaller spans of around 18/460 mm a cheaper, pointed roof will use plain bricks or slabs with a single cut shape in the center. For larger spans it is also possible to use standard bricks by building the arch over a former and filling the gaps between with a refractory cement and aggregate. An arch inevitably exerts outward pressure along each side. A firm top layer of brick should extend out to the metal of the framework which can be usefully strengthened at this level. See Diagram 38. The pressure could slowly crush some of the softer insulators. It will be necessary to fill above the arch with insulating cement or loose filling

Ill. 19. A small top-loader with one roof batt and first row of bricks in place. Standing in front is the cased insulating roof layer of Caposil and asbestos sheet as shown in Diagram 33. The shrinkage of the block will cause surface cracks but I have not found these to be a serious drawback.

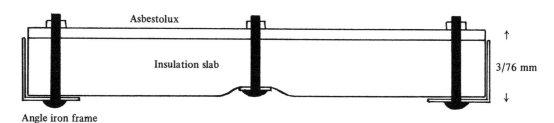

Asbestolux

Insulation slab

3/76 mm

Angle iron frame

Diag. 33. A section through the cased insulation for roof as shown in the photograph. The outer bolts hold the block between angle and top sheet. The center bolt carries a large washer under the head and is tightened sufficiently to pull it flush with the rest of the surface.

such as crushed insulating brick (the waste from the kiln building), alumina bubbles, vermiculite, etc. This is topped up to 4/100 mm or so thick, or levelled with the top of the arch, and covered with insulating slabs. The whole is then covered with sheet metal or asbestos. An average arch rise is 2 inches to a foot of span—50 to 300 mm.

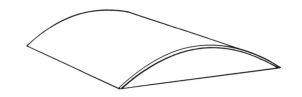

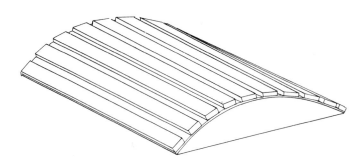

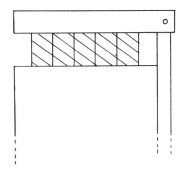

Diag. 34. Side view of the cased insulation slab hinged from extensions of the upright corner members of the frame. Slab must be positioned to lie flat on the hot-face brick layer, to facilitate this, and to allow for heat expansion, a vertically slotted hole can be cut in the upright member.

Diag. 36. An arch is built over a 'former' made from hardboard or slats nailed over arch-shaped wooden ends. It is supported on pillars of brick or other material, and the whole is removed once the mortar is set.

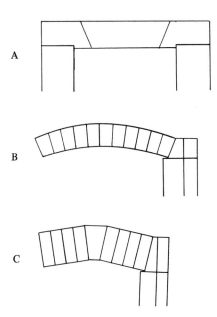

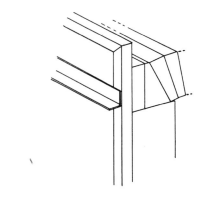

Diag. 37. The outward thrust of an arch makes it advisable to strengthen the side walls with an extra length of angle iron.

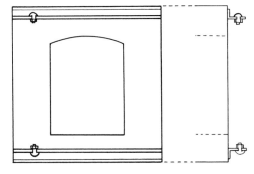

Diag. 35. A. A type of roof found in commercial kilns (see Ill. 2) using slabs of H.T. Insulating brick, which are available in sizes up to 18/455 mm × 4.5/115 × 9/225 mm.
B. Standard arch using arch bricks and skewbacks. This will give a rather high curve and the arch bricks can alternate with squares (standards) in smaller kilns.
C. A simple inverted-V roof using standard bricks and a cut keystone. See also Spec. 4 at end of book.

Diag. 38. The door is hinged between the two bolts, or on a rod at the same position.

DOOR·

The easiest method of door construction in front-loaders for the amateur builder is to cut and assemble bricks for the aperture, and to fit and dismantle them at each firing. This will involve two layers unless the bricks are laid 9/228 mm deep for it is sometimes overlooked that the door should have as much insulation as the rest of the kiln. Lightweight insulators for the outer skin of the door can be cased as described for the roof of top-loaders. Brick, 3/75 or $4\frac{1}{2}$/ 114 mm, would then be sufficient.

Hinged doors represent the most considerable engineering feature of the average kiln.

If a fully cased-up door is to be made, its weight should, when closed, be taken by a sill. This can be a length of angle iron across the front of the kiln below the aperture. A second length above the door will ensure a rigid hinge. The door is hinged between the two bolts on the left of the opening as in Diagram 39.

The door itself is usually built of brick, but ceramic fiber is a lighter alternative. Frequently, because of the weight problem, a brick door is only $4\frac{1}{2}$/114 mm thick which results in heat loss and uneven chamber temperature. A door frame of angle iron must be welded at the corners; a bolted frame is unlikely to take the diagonal strain. The bricks are held in place by metal rods (ideally of a stainless or rustless steel) which are passed through the door frame and then either through holes in the bricks or set in grooves in the brick courses. Fred Olsen recommends a flange on the frame to engage a slot cut in each edge brick.

The door should overlap the front face of the aperture. The degree of overlap depends on how deeply the door is cut to enter the chamber. See Illustration 2 for a highly professional door.

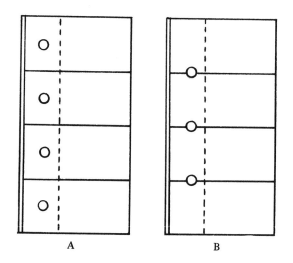

Diag. 39. Section through a kiln door showing position of rods which are fastened at each end to the metal frame of the door and pass through either (A) the brick centers, or (B) in grooves between brick layers.

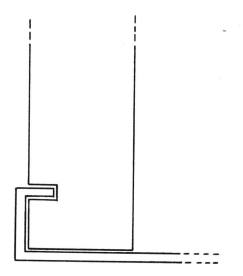

Diag. 40. A return flange on the door frame holds all the outer door bricks in place.

Any section through the door should have at least two-thirds, and preferably the whole, of the insulation value of the walls. A hinged door, unless it is to be cut to hold elements, is surely the ideal place for the new ceramic fiber materials. High-temperature board of 1/25 mm can be glued with the special H.T. adhesive made for the purpose to a backing of lower temperature insulation mineral-wool block.

Pins and ceramic cups as described in Diagram 22 on p. 37 could be used in addition to tie the materials to the framework or to a cladding of metal or asbestos sheet. This type of door would have only a fraction of the weight of a brick one.

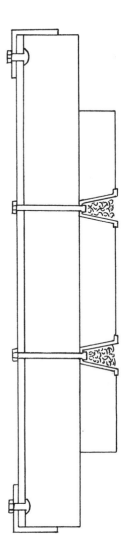

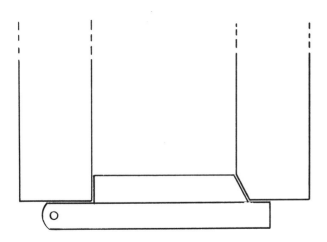

Diag. 41. Door inset.

Diag. 42. A lightweight door using ceramic fiber. A high temperature fiber slab 2/51 mm thick is adhered with special glue (Fiberfix, etc.) to 3 inches of mineral-wool block with additional strengthening of ceramic cups bolted through to Asbestolux or Sindanyo. The asbestos sheet is itself bolted to the angle iron frame.

ELEMENT HOUSING

COILED-WIRE ELEMENTS

The coils must be fully supported and prevented from touching one another. The slots or cradles can be cut into H.T. insulating brick with an ordinary saw, though the bricks are very abrasive and will soon wear the saw smooth. Replaceable-blade saws such as Eclipse are useful but if you can recut the teeth of an old cross-cut or pruning saw, this is even better. One can also use drill attachments.

A simple, square, horizontal groove is not satisfactory. Coils move during firing and will soon fall out of the slots (at worst, short-circuiting to the one below). The ideal shape for an element slot is shown in Diagram 43. The opening should be only just large enough to accept the coil with a little pressure, but there must be room for it to dissipate its heat when in place. If three cuts are made with a saw and the saw then set into the center cut, it can be rocked to and fro, snapping off the two adjacent sections which can then be withdrawn.

If the top slot is too near the roof-batt recess this will weaken the brick which may eventually break away. Since the top element should be as close to the roof as possible the section shown in Diagram 45 is recommended. Slots for the vertical sections of hairpin elements should be cut as deeply as those for coils but they can, of course, be much narrower. Two possible sections are shown in Diagram 46. If the section on the right is used, the coil should be a little short so that it can be stretched and sprung into the groove. Note: Wire expands considerably during the early stages of firing. One might be tempted to lay a straight length of wire in a slot in order to bring all mains connections to one end but this is inadvisable as the wire will buckle into a wide arc which may bring it into contact with another element and so fuse the whole system.

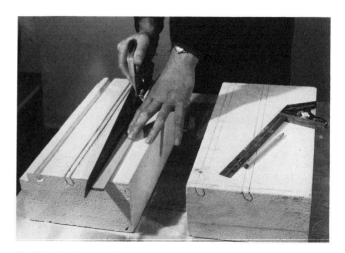

Ill. 20. Cutting slots for elements.

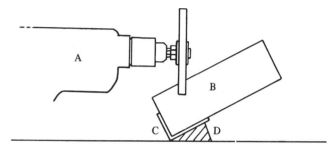

Diag. 44. A system of cutting slots with a drill and grinding wheel as developed by Mike Harris. The drill (A) is clamped into position. The brick (B) is guided by a length of angle iron (C) which is tilted and fastened to a block (D) so that the grinding wheel cuts a groove to the required depth. By extension the system can be used to cut more than one slot in a brick face. Slots will line up very accurately. This method produces a lot of dust, so wear a mask!

Diag. 43. The ideal shape for an element slot.

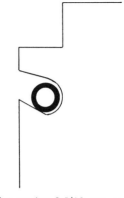

Diag. 45. Top slot section 0.5/13 mm or so below the roof batt rebate.

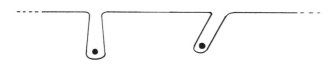

Diag. 46. Upright slots for hairpin elements.

Ill. 21. The turning tool for routing slots. The bevel on this one has been worn away; it has been used on many dozens of slots.

Ill. 23. A short length of wire coil (preferably 13 swg) is a useful tool for shaping and smoothing slots.

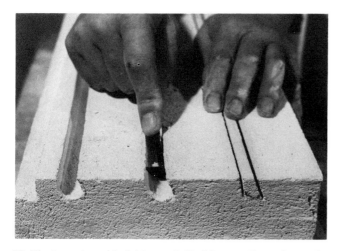

Ill. 22. A turning tool of this type is ideal for rounding and smoothing the inner faces of the element slots.

Ill. 24. If the slots are cut so that the openings barely accept the coils the latter can be tapped into place using a small strip of wood as shown here. The elements are then less likely to spring out.

57

It is possible to cast walls or sections complete with slots. An average aggregate is four volumes of crushed firebrick or H.T. insulating brick to one of H.T. aluminous cement such as Ciment Fondu, Monocast 125/200, etc. The casting set-up is shown in Diagram 47.

A wooden box is constructed and screwed together, of the size and depth of the required wall section. The depth can be about 2/50 mm. Two sides are drilled near the top to take greased rods of wood or metal and of the diameter of the required element slots (element coil plus 33–50 percent). The concrete is well-mixed and should not be too sloppy. The manufacturers' instructions must be followed. It is advisable to soak the aggregate and then drain before adding the cement. The box is now filled with the concrete until the rods are almost covered. It is well tamped down. As soon as it begins to set (about two hours) the rods are carefully withdrawn. When hard, the box is unscrewed and the panel withdrawn. The sharp edges of the grooves are rasped smooth and slightly rounded: the openings should just accept the wire coils. Alternatively the panel can be cast face down, in which case a fillet or bead is fastened to the box floor beneath each rod to form the opening. This gives a firmer edge to the slot. Cast holders are usually limited to firings up to 1200/2190°T.

A third system employs white refractory supports which fit into the wall and can be cemented into place. A press-mold can be used to form the strips.

There are many involved and expensive systems of element support used in industrial kilns and for special purposes. Those illustrated in the Kanthal Handbook themselves build up to form the hot-face wall. Insulating bricks can be cut as in Diagram 50 and built up in a similar way.

Of all these methods the saw-cut style is the simplest and one of the most effective. The surface of the groove should be finished as smooth as possible or the element coils will catch on the rough parts as they expand and contract causing them to bunch up at certain points along their length. A wash with high alumina cement may help. Beware of silica cements as these may damage the elements. Rhodes suggests a mixture of calcined alumina and kaolin.

Preformed blocks of ceramic fiber with slots provided are available. These are rather soft and need careful handling. See Illustration 6 on page 38.

It is possible to accommodate coils in the roof of a kiln. The coils must be of the hairpin type and are installed from the front of the kiln, as in Diagram 51.

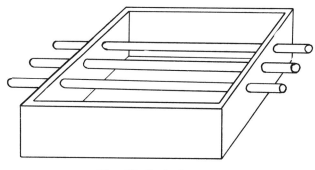

Diag. 47. Casting box.

Casting box section

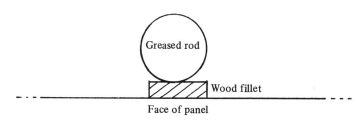

Diag. 48. Side view of casting with panel face down, showing fillet or bead fastened to box floor.

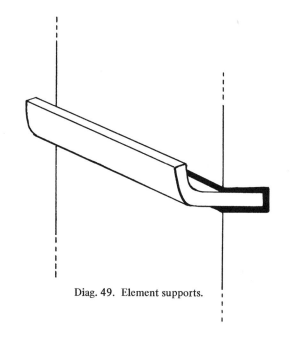

Diag. 49. Element supports.

58

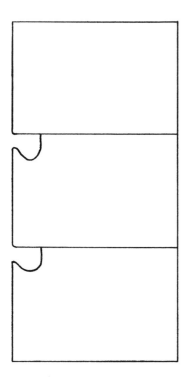

Diag. 50. Cut corner bricks to support elements.

Diag. 51. Hairpin coils in kiln roof.

TAIL HOLES

To bring the element tails to the outside of the kiln for connection to each other or to the mains, holes must be drilled through the kiln walls. It is best to drill these from the inside when the kiln is assembled. An electric drill is almost essential; it is a very slow job with a ratchet brace. If a long enough bit is not available, one can easily be made from a length of metal rod.

The hole entrances in the chamber will sometimes be quite close together, especially at the corners of top-loaders, but if the exit holes on the outside of the kiln are less than 1.5/38 mm apart the connectors could come into contact, with dire results. The holes should therefore be sloped apart as shown in Diagram 52. When drilling is done from the inside, as is recommended, the angle between the drill holes will occur naturally.

Ill. 25. A homemade tail-hole bit.

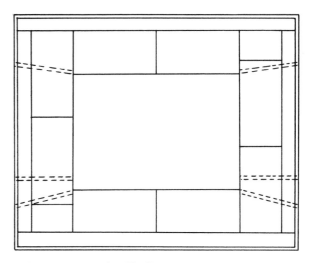

Diag. 52. Sloped tail holes.

SPYHOLES AND VENTILATION

The placing of spyholes for ventilation and for watching the cone will depend on your normal type of pack. You do not want to have to build tottering piles of supports for the cone. I have found, for a mixed tableware and one-off pack, that a position 5/125 mm to 6/150 mm below the roof and about one-third of the way along the door or the longer wall of a top-loader is convenient. This allows jugs and pots or two layers of bowls at the top of the kiln, and the cone is sited on a shelf and not between two. Try to visualize a pack before you decide where to drill the spyhole. The asbestos can be cut with an expanding drill bit, and a hole an inch or so across drilled through the wall which is then reamed out with an old knife, rasp, or other tool to the shape and size required. The most convenient shape for a spyhole is shown in Diagram 53 and gives minimum aperture with maximum angle of sight-lines (dotted). A purpose made bung can be thrown to fit.

A dry-built top-loader will usually let smoke and steam out during firing. The lid can be slightly propped up for preliminary burning off of wax etc. which will often take an hour or more. Front-loaders are often built with a loose brick top back or in the roof, or you could form a funnel-shaped hole with a bung similar to the spyhole. If a door safety switch is fitted, this is essential.

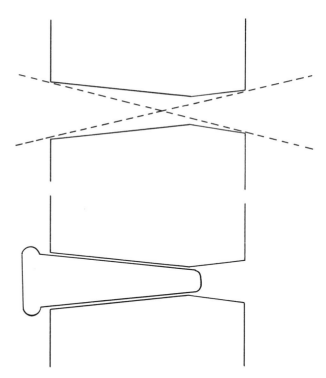

Diag. 53. Spyhole sight-lines and bung.

SILICON-CARBIDE RODS

These rods are freestanding though they may be protected by being run in wide slots in the brickwork or between brick ledges as shown in the specifications given for kiln 4 in Chapter 10.

If rods stand out in the kiln, the danger of accidental breakage during packing or drawing a kiln is always present. They can be protected by means of a sheet of board or asbestos, ideally dropped into slots to hold it in place.

The tail holes for rods must be drilled more carefully than is necessary for the pliable wire tails. Any stress from movement of the layers of insulation relative to one another through a wall thickness may break the rod. The holes must therefore give good clearance to the rods and should be carefully lined up with an appropriate wooden dowel.

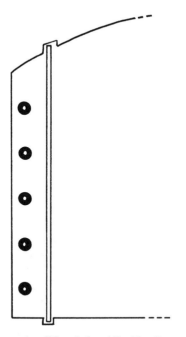

Diag. 54. Protecting SiC rods in a kiln. The diagram illustrates how a sheet of hardboard or similar material can be slid into position when packing or drawing the kiln and withdrawn for firing. This shows a front-loader but the arrangement for a top-loader would be similar.

6. Calculation and Design of Heating Elements

CALCULATION

Perhaps the most daunting aspect of electric kiln building is the calculation of the elements. An understanding of the principles and their application is not, however, beyond anyone who gives a little thought to the matter.

Electrical theory was discussed in Chapter 3. The use of the basic equations listed there, together with an appreciation of the need for the element to be able to radiate all the power which is being generated (see p 64), can cope with almost any situation.

To repeat two equations from Chapter 3:

$$\text{Current I (in amperes A)} = \frac{\text{Power } P \text{ (in watts W)}}{\text{Force } E \text{ (in volts V)}}$$

$$\text{Current I (in amperes A)} = \frac{\text{Force } E \text{ (in volts V)}}{\text{Resistance } R \text{ (in ohms } \Omega)}$$

By switching these about we can get the ten additional relationships listed in Table 2 on p 21.

Calculations can conveniently start with one fixed factor: the *voltage* of your mains supply. It is possible to alter voltage through transformers but this is rarely practiced outside the factory. Most kiln circuits are between line and neutral in England (240 V) and between line and line (120 V each) in the U.S.

The second figure to be ascertained is the maximum current available (amperes). This is controlled by the capacity of the wires connecting your workshop to the mains supply cables.

On a household installation in England the maximum single point of supply is usually the 'cooker' circuit rated at 30 amperes (recently raised to 45A). You may be able to get a special line installed from which you can take more current—say 50 amperes. If a three-phase supply is available it usually has a capacity of 50 amperes-plus per line, and will likely take any load you may want to connect to it.

From these two ascertainable values, voltage and current, you can derive a third figure—the *power* in watts—by simply multiplying them together.

EXAMPLE 1.
Derived from the current possibilities mentioned above and assuming voltage to be 240 then:

240 × 30 = 7200 watts (7.2 kW) maximum power
240 × 50 = 12000 watts (12 kW) maximum power
240 × 50 × 3 (phases) = 36000 watts (35 kW) or more.

So we now have values for E, I, and P in the equations given above, and can deduce the value of R in a given situation.

Referring again to Chapter 3, you see that heat is produced by the resistance of the element wire to the passage of current, and that the degree of resistance is measured in ohms. Each unit length of a resistance wire or rod exerts a given number of ohms according to the square of its diameter. The unit of length is generally a foot or a meter. The total resistance is the figure per unit of length multiplied by the number of units, e.g., 0.1 ohms per foot over 100 feet of wire exert $100 \times 0.1 = 10$ ohms; 135 feet would exert 13.5 ohms, and so on. (Note: The figure 0.1 is approximate resistance per foot of 13 swg Kanthal A1: the precise figure is 0.103.) Conversely we can divide the total ohms by the resistance per unit length to find the overall length of wire needed. In a circuit of 11 ohms resistance, using wire with a resistance of 0.16 ohms per foot, then $\dfrac{11}{0.16} = 68.75$ feet of wire.

TABLE 7
Resistance Figures for Kanthal A1 Wire

Gauge	No.	Ohms of Resistance per foot	Ohms of Resistance per meter
SWG	11	0.065	0.019
AWG	9	0.067	0.020
SWG	12	0.081	0.025
AWG	10	0.084	0.026
SWG	13	0.103	0.031
AWG	11	0.106	0.032
AWG	12	0.133	0.040
SWG	14	0.136	0.041
AWG	13	0.168	0.051
SWG	15	0.168	0.051
AWG	14	0.212	0.065
SWG	16	0.213	0.065
AWG	15	0.268	0.082
SWG	17	0.278	0.085
AWG	16	0.338	0.103
SWG	18	0.379	0.116

Divide total ohms value of a circuit by appropriate figure in table to arrive at total wire length required in feet or meters.

EXAMPLE 2.
Assuming you have 50 amperes at 240 volts:

$$R = \frac{E}{I} = \frac{240}{50} = 4.8 \text{ ohms.}$$

With wire resistance of 0.1 ohms per foot:

$$\frac{4.8}{0.1} = 48 \text{ feet of wire to produce 12 kW.}$$

All values derived from the equations will be *electrically* valid but not all will be *practically applicable* to the use of resistance wire or rod. This is because the element *must have sufficient surface area to dissipate the energy produced*. This factor is known as heat-dissipation or watt-loss and is discussed in detail on p 64. If you apply this criterion to Example 2, which looks like a nice cheap circuit, you find that the wire would burn out in a very short time because the wattage per square inch of surface would be more than it could dissipate. All figures must therefore be checked against the watt-loss diagrams to see that the resistance material (the same principle applies to silicon-carbide rods) can endure the load put upon it.

When a straight-forward calculation of $\dfrac{E}{I} = R$ gives an impractical result as in Example 2, what can be done? In this example the resistance figure was obviously too low. The voltage figure being fixed at 240, the only way to increase R is by passing less current. If you halve the current to 25 amperes, then $\dfrac{240}{25} = 9.6$ ohms: $\dfrac{9.6}{0.1} = 96$ ft (29 m) of wire. By reducing the current to one-third of its original value: $\dfrac{240}{16.7} = 14.4$ or 144 feet of the same gauge wire. The 25-amperes calculation giving 96 feet is within the limits of practicality and could be used for earthenware firing; the second figure of 144 feet is applicable to any type of kiln.

Having reduced the current, the power produced declines by the same amount, e.g., the two-thirds reduction gives $240 \times 16.7 = 4$ kW. To build up to the original 12 kW you must use *three separate circuits* in parallel (see p 23), each producing 4 kW.

In summation then, calling the resistance per unit length of wire RU, and the final length of circuit, X:

$$\frac{E}{I} = R, \quad \text{and,} \quad \frac{R}{RU} = X$$

In practice it is advisable to keep the current limit at about 25 amperes; the most useful range is 15–20 amperes. The figure for X must be checked against the watt-loss Table 8 (p. 64) and a value for watts per square inch (or centimeter) of surface is needed to do this. Again, it is easier to work this out in two stages. Let PU indicate watts per unit of length, and Z the surface area per unit of length. The latter can be found in the appropriate column in the Table on p. 64. This gives two more equations:

$$\frac{P}{X} = PU, \text{ and, } \frac{PU}{Z} = \text{ Watts per sq. inch or sq. cm. according to whether X represents feet or meters.}$$

EXAMPLE 3.

A small kiln requiring 4.5 kW to fire to 1260/2300°T on 240 volts, using 14 swg Kanthal A1 wire (0.136 ohms per foot).

current required $\dfrac{4500}{240} = 18.75$ amperes

resistance required $\dfrac{240}{18.75} = 12.8$ ohms

wire length $\dfrac{12.8}{0.136} = 94$ feet (29 m)

watts per foot $\dfrac{4500}{94} = 47.9$ watts

square inches per foot length as in Table 8 = 3.02

watts per in^2 $\dfrac{47.9}{3.02} = 15.9$

Checking on the watt-loss chart it will be seen that 15.9 is outside the limits of safety for a firing temperature of 1260°C—in fact it is very near the limit for any glaze firing. Some variation in the design is necessary. A slightly smaller kiln with a 4 kW load gives a figure of 14 W/in^2 which would be adequate in a well-built kiln. To split the load into two circuits as suggested in a previous calculation would give a total wire length of 376/115 m which would be almost impossible to house in a small kiln.

The other possible solution, if voltage and load are fixed, is to vary the wire gauge. A thinner wire with more resistance will make matters worse, so at least the next gauge thicker—13 swg which has 0.103 ohms of resistance per ft. and a surface area of 3.47 in^2/ft—will have to be used.

EXAMPLE 4.

Starting from the third equation in Example 3:

wire length $\dfrac{12.8}{0.103} = 124$ feet

watts/foot $\dfrac{4500}{124} = 36.3$

watts/in.^{2} $\dfrac{36.3}{3.47} = 10.46$

This last figure is satisfactory and means that all the calculations are valid and that 124/37.8 m of 13 swg Kanthal A1 in a single circuit will give the required 4500 watts of power with a good wire-life expectancy. The 124 feet will, of course, be split up into a number of shorter lengths which will be wound into coils to fit conveniently into the element slots provided in the kiln walls with each piece, or element, connected to the next in series.

EXAMPLE 5.

Example 4 indicated that 4500 watts was the maximum which could be used in one circuit at stoneware temperatures. If a larger kiln, 6.5 kW, 240 volts, is used, therefore, it will be necessary to split the wiring into two circuits, each of 3.25 kW.

$\dfrac{3250}{240} = 13.54$ amps

$\dfrac{240}{13.54} = 17.7$ ohms

$\dfrac{17.7}{0.103} = 171$ feet

$\dfrac{3250}{171} = 19$ W/ft

$\dfrac{19}{3.47} = 5.5.$ W/in^2

These figures are reasonably satisfactory but the total wire is 171/52 m per circuit or 342/104 m in all. This is an expensive answer and would cram the kiln full of wire. There is plenty of latitude on the W/in^2 figure so, reverse the operation in Example 3 and try substituting a thinner wire. Repeating the sums for 14 swg you get: $\dfrac{17.7}{0.136} \times 2$

(circuits) = 260/79 m in all, with a watt-loss figure of 8.3. The two circuits would be wired independently, in parallel.

Larger kilns with ratings of 12 kW and upwards will normally require a three-phase supply. The load is then split ideally into three circuits or multiples of three, though this is not always convenient and one may have to put double the load on one phase compared with the others. The principles of calculation are still those outlined above. For instance a kiln taking 27 kW could be powered by six circuits, two on a phase, each of 4500 watts. The wire length for 13 swg, as worked out in Example 4 is 124/38 m, thus the total wire required would be 124 × 6 = 744/227 m.

TABLE 8
Surface Area of Kanthal Wire for
Watt-loss Calculations

Gauge	No.	in²/ft	cm²/m (approx.)
SWG	11	4.37	91.00
AWG	9	4.31	90.00
SWG	12	3.92	83.00
AWG	10	3.84	81.00
SWG	13	3.47	73.00
AWG	11	3.42	72.00
AWG	12	3.05	63.00
SWG	14	3.02	63.00
AWG	13	2.71	57.00
SWG	15	2.71	57.00
AWG	14	2.42	51.00
SWG	16	2.41	51.00
AWG	15	2.15	45.00
SWG	17	2.11	44.00
AWG	16	1.92	40.00

Divide total wattage of a circuit by feet or meters of wire used, and the resultant figure by the appropriate surface area figure in the table. This gives watts per in² or cm² which can be checked against Graph 7.

WATT-LOSS (HEAT DISSIPATION)

Heat produced by an electrical resistance material is a continuing process and energy must be released at a rate which will balance the input, otherwise heat will build up until the material melts. This balance is worked out by reference to the surface area of the wire or rod which is, of course, that part of the material which radiates the heat into the surrounding air, or kiln brick in contact with it. Since the heat relates to the electrical power applied to the material as expressed in watts, the process is known as watt-loss. The surface area of a wire or rod is arrived at by multiplying the diameter by 3.14 (pi) and by a unit of length of the wire or rod. Table 8 presents figures for cm² per meter, and in² per foot.

The limits of power which Kanthal wire will stand without damage are summed up in Graph 7 which is derived from that in the Kanthal Handbook.

To use the diagram, draw a vertical line from the temperature at which you wish to fire, and a horizontal line from the surface area figure arrived at through the equations discussed in the previous section. The point where they cross should lie within the white area. It will be seen that the higher the temperature, the greater is the surface area needed to dissipate the heat. This is because the difference between the element temperature and that of the surrounding air and brick in the firing chamber becomes smaller as the firing temperature rises. We can personally experience this phenomenon in the difficulty of getting rid of body heat in midsummer compared with midwinter.

To return to Graph 7, the vertical line X from 1060/1940°T intersects the limit curve at 15: W/in² (watts per square inch) for Kanthal A, and at 21.2 for A1 (stressing the superior heat-resisting properties of the latter). Vertical line Y at 1275/2320°T, falls completely outside the range of A and reduces the limit of A1 to 10 W/in². Line Z from 1325/2410°T lies outside the limits of either.

By reversing the sums shown in the earlier section of this chapter you can work back to wire lengths and so to power limits.

EXAMPLE 6.

We can see in Graph 7 that a suitable rating for a 1250/2280°T firing would be 10.3 W/in². Using 14 swg A1, then: W/in² × in²/ft = w/ft. In this case: 10.3 × 3.02 = 31.1. Thus 100 feet of wire can dissipate 100 × 31.1 = 3110 watts of power.

Graph 7. Watt-loss graphs by kind permission Kanthal Ltd.

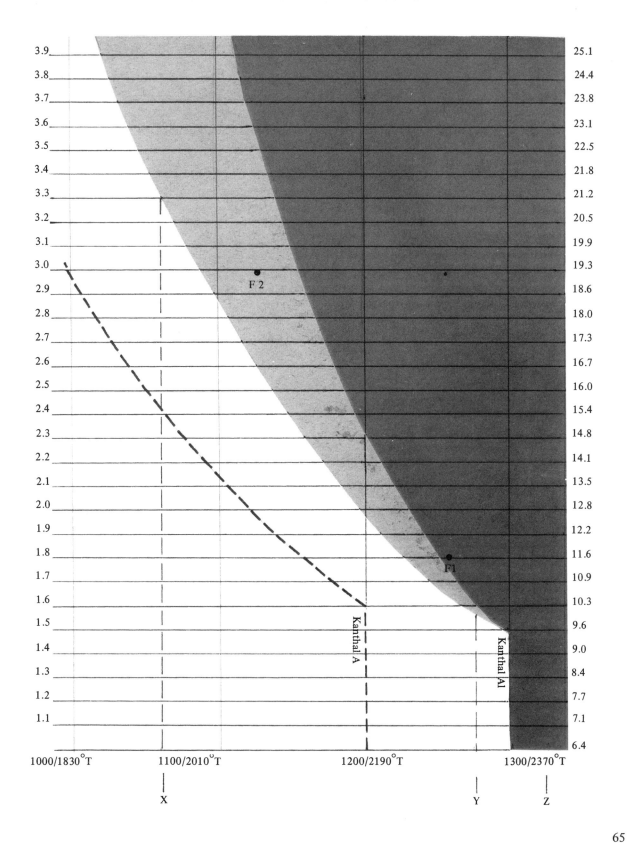

There is only one point where the figure arrived at in this way will correspond with the power actually generated by the wire at a given voltage but the calculation is useful as a guide to where this may lie. Graph 8 illustrates this point.

The *Kanthal Handbook* also makes the point that the limits can be exceeded "under ideal conditions." For pottery kilns these probably include loose-fitting element slots so that coils have plenty of air round them, and the coils themselves stretched to 1.5 diameters or more (see p. 81). It has been found in practice that a factor of 1.25 can operate at lower temperatures, decreasing to nil at about 1275/2325°T. Applying this extension to the watt-loss Graph 7 gives the light gray area which can be accepted as being in the range of practical application. It is still true, however, that a lower watt-load will lengthen the life of the coil. One of my own kilns operates on about 118/36 m of Kanthal A1 13 swg generating 4,750 watts on 240 volts. There are three such circuits. This is represented by point F1 in Graph 7 and the element life has been satisfactory with regular firings up to 1265/2310°T. A kiln for earthenware at 1130/2070°T has been operating on 90 feet of the same gauge wire (F2 in Graph 7) for seven years on the original elements.

So far all calculations have been on the basis of a 240 V supply. In many places the voltage may be less and, although the foregoing equations still hold good, slightly different problems are posed.

EXAMPLE 7.
Using the data from Example 3 but changing the voltage from 240 to 120 V the following figures result:

$$\frac{4500}{120} = 37.5 \text{ amperes}$$

$$\frac{120}{37.5} = 3.2 \text{ ohms}$$

$$\frac{3.2}{0.103} = 31 \text{ feet of wire (13 swg)}$$

$$\frac{4500}{31} = 145 \text{ W/ft}$$

$$\frac{145}{3.47} = 41.8 \text{ W/in}^2$$

These figures are patently inapplicable. A very much thicker wire would give better answers but be equally impracticable. The power must be drastically reduced to bring the watt-loss to a reasonable figure.

EXAMPLE 8.
Consider using two circuits in parallel each with half the power, e.g., 2,500 watts each. Each circuit then has a resistance of 2 X 3.2 = 6.4 ohms.

$$\frac{6.4}{0.103} = 62 \text{ feet}$$

$$\frac{2250}{62} = 36 \text{ W/ft}$$

$$\frac{36}{3.47} = 10.4 \text{ W/in}^2$$

This is reasonable for temperatures up to around 1265/2310°T. We can guess that 2,000 watts would be ideal and, in fact, produces figures of 70/21 m of wire with 8.24 as watt-loss figure. For high stoneware firings the sensible procedure would be to use two or three 2 kW-circuits (total 4,000 or 6,000 watts) and to design the size of kiln accordingly. Adequate results can be attained with thinner wires; 15 swg, for instance, will need 68.5/20.9 m to produce 1.25 kW with a watt-loss figure of 6.8.

To sum up, for lower voltages a greater number of parallel circuits must be used, each providing from 1.25 kW to 2.25 kW of the total power required.

Having worked out a suitable wire length for your purposes you must be sure that the total length of the element slots proposed in your kiln plan is sufficient to hold the length of coil which will result from winding the wire. This can be worked out through the following formulas. All the calculations presume there is a 1.25 diameter space between coils (see Chapter 6, p. 81). The letter 'd' indicates diameter.

A. To find the length of slot which will be spanned by a given length of wire wound into coils.
1. length of a single coil = (mandrel diameter + wire diameter) X 3.14 (pi)
2. total wire divided by coil length = number of coils
3. number of coils X wire d X 2.25 = slot length (S_1)
These stages can be combined in one equation:

$$\frac{W_1}{(M_d + W_d) \times \text{pi}} \times W_d \times 2.25 = S_1$$

W_1 refers to wire length; M_d mandrel diameter; W_d wire diameter. The figure of 2.25 represents the increase in length when a close-wound coil is stretched out to 1.25d between coils, i.e., to 2.25 times its original length.

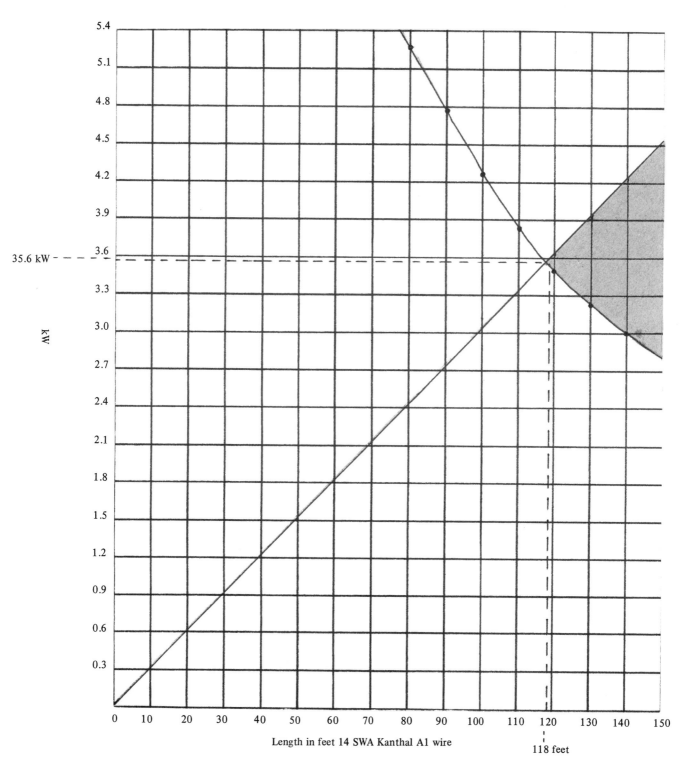

Graph 8. Watt-loss and current graph. The straight line traces the watt-loss/power ratios for various lengths of 14 swg A1 wire. Example: 100 feet can dissipate 3016 watts at 10 watts per in². The curved line indicates the actual power generated by various lengths of wire at 240V. Example: 80 teet generates 5286 watts. The lines meet at 118 ft/3556 watts. The shaded area is one of rapidly increasing watt-loss and decreasing power.

EXAMPLE 9.

15 feet of 13 swg wire wound on a three-eighth inch mandrel:

1. $(0.375 + .092) \times 3.14 = 1.47$ in
2. $\dfrac{(15 \times 12)}{1.47} = 122$ coils
3. $122 \times .092 \times 2.25 = 25.25$ inch slot.

Or using the equation above:

$\dfrac{180 \text{ (in)}}{.467 \times 3.14} \times .092 \times 2.25 = 122 \times .092 \times 2.25 = 25.25/$ 647 mm slot

Metric units work the same way: using 4.57 m of wire on 9.5 mm mandrel (similar sizes to previous example):

$\dfrac{4570}{(9.5 + 2.34) \times 3.14} \times 2.34 \times 2.25 = 647$ mm slot

B. To find maximum length of wire which, when wound into coils, can be housed in a given slot length.

1. $\dfrac{\text{slot length}}{2.25} = $ length of close-wound coils
2. $\dfrac{\text{length of close coils}}{\text{diameter of wire}} = $ number of coils
3. (mandrel diameter + wire diameter) $\times$ 3.14 (pi) = length of a single coil
4. number of coils $\times$ length of a coil = wire length

As a single equation:

$$\dfrac{\left(\dfrac{S_1}{2.25}\right)}{W_d} \times [(M_d + W_d) \times \text{pi}] = \text{wire length}$$

EXAMPLE 10.

As in Example 9: 25 inches of slot, 13 swg wire, three-eighth-inch mandrel.

1. $\dfrac{25}{2.25} = 11.1$
2. $\dfrac{11.1}{.092} = 121$
3. $(.375 + .092) \times 3.14 = 1.47$
4. $121 \times 1.47 = 177$ inches or 14.8 feet of wire

The slight discrepancy is because we started with 25 inches instead of 25.25 inches as precise length from Example 9.

These Examples refer to a single slot or a hairpin element for 12.5 inch slots. The same formula is used to decide the total slot length required for an entire circuit.

EXAMPLE 11.

34.7 m of 13 awg wire wound on a 6.5 mm mandrel. Using system A above:

$\dfrac{34700}{(6.5 + 1.83) \times 3.14} \times 1.83 \times 2.25$

$\dfrac{34700}{26.156} \times 1.83 \times 2.25$

$1327 \times 1.83 \times 2.25 = 5464$ mm of slot.

SUMMARY

1. Find out the voltage and maximum current available.
2. Within the current limit decide on the total power to be used to fire the kiln to the working temperature required. The power/volume graph on p. 43 will help.
3. Using Table 10 as a guide, decide on the number of circuits to be used and divide the total power by this number.
4. Make trial calculations and decide on the wire gauge.
5. Work out the length of wire per circuit.
6. Check against watt-loss diagram.
7. Multiply the length of wire per circuit by the number of circuits and ascertain that you can house it all in the number of slots you have planned in the kiln, or better still, plan your kiln and element slots to take the total length of stretched element coil.

A rather involved-looking equation is given in the *Kanthal Handbook* by means of which the correct wire diameter (gauge) for an element can be calculated:

$$d = \frac{1}{K_d} \sqrt[3]{\left(\frac{P}{E}\right)^2 \times \frac{q}{p}}$$

Some of these symbols are familiar: P for wattage; E for voltage; d for diameter. For the rest: K_d equals 335.3 by calculating in the inch system, or 2.91 in the metric system; q equals specific resistance in ohms per cir. mil ft or mm^2/m at the working temperature of the appropriate Kanthal alloy; p equals permissible surface load in watts. The resistance of A1 at $20/68°T$ is 872 ohms per cir. mil foot at $1300/2370°T$, 908 ohms. The permissible surface load at $1300/2370°T$ is 10 W/in^2.

TABLE 9

Gauge	Length of Single Coil	Length of Slot Occupied by 10/3.05 m of Wire	Length of Wire in 10/3.05 m Slot
	on .375/9.5 mm mandrel		
12 SWG	1.5/38 mm	18.7/477 mm	64/19.5
13 SWG	1.47/37.3 mm	16.9/429 mm	21/21.6 m
11 AWG	1.46/37.1 mm	16.7/426 mm	71/21.6 m
12 AWG	1.43/36 mm	15.25/387 mm	78.6/24 m
14 SWG	1.43/36 mm	15.25/385 mm	78.6/24 m
	on .25/6.5 mm mandrel		
13 AWG / 15 SWG	1.0/26 mm	19.25/488 mm	62.4/19 m
14 AWG / 16 SWG	0.986/25 mm	17.54/446 mm	68.4/20.86 m

TABLE 10

Load/Circuits/Feet Kanthal A1 Wire on 240 V

Watts	Gauge Group	Circuits	Feet (Total)	W/in²	Recommended Max. Temp.
2500	A	1	107	9.6	1200/2190
3000	B	1	114	9.7	1250/2280
3500	C	1	122	9.5	1270/2320
3500	D	1	158	6.4	1280/2340
4000	C	1	107	12.4	1240/2265
4000	D	1	138	8.4	1280/2340
4500	D	1	123	10.6	1280/2340
5000	D	1	111	13.0	1275/2325
6000	B	2	228	9.7	1250/2280
7000	C	2	244	9.5	1270/2320
8000	C	2	214	12.4	1240/2265
8000	D	2	276	8.4	1280/2340
9000	D	2	246	10.6	1280/2340
10,000	D	2	222	13.0	1275/2325
12,000	C	3	321	12.4	1240/2265
12,000	D	3	414	8.4	1280/2340
13,500	D	3	369	10.6	1280/2340
15,000	D	3	333	13.0	1275/2325

Table 10 may be continued indefinitely by multiplication.

The Gauge Groups are:

A	16 SWG 14 AWG
B	15 SWG 13 AWG
C	14 SWG 12 AWG
D	13 SWG 11 AWG

The figures are therefore a compromise between these gauges, but are sufficiently accurate as a guide.

EXAMPLE 12.

Entering these figures in the formula and working on 5000 watts load at 240 W you get:

$$d = \frac{1}{335} \sqrt[3]{\frac{5000^2}{240} \times \frac{908}{10}} = \frac{1}{335}$$

$$\sqrt[3]{433 \times 90.8} = \frac{1}{335} \times 34 = .1015 \text{ inches diameter}$$

This figure is between 10 and 11 awg, or, between 12 and 13 swg, confirming the choice made through other calculations and considerations for high temperature elements elsewhere in this book.

A shorter equation which fulfills the same purpose refers to the figures in Table 14 at the end of the book marked cm^2/Ω and $in^2 \Omega$: $\dfrac{I^2 \times Ct}{p}$

I is, of course, amperes; Ct refers to the increase of resistance with temperature in the last column of the Table; p is the permissible load in cm^2/m or $1 m^2/ft$ (see watt-loss).

EXAMPLE 13.

Using the same data as in longer equation:

$$I = \frac{P}{E} = \frac{5000}{240} = 20.8 \text{ amperes}$$

$$\frac{20.8^2 \times 1.042}{10} = 45.08$$

Looking up 45.08 in Table 14 you find, as previously, between 12 and 13 swg.

INCREASE OF RESISTANCE WITH TEMPERATURE

All the foregoing calculations have been based on the nominal quoted wire resistance at $20/68°T$. This resistance increases as the wire gets hotter. Consequently less power is produced just when it is needed most and this is a secondary cause of the 'spent rocket' curve of a typical temp/hrs firing graph. The loss is not enough to be serious unless the power/volume ratio is near its limit, but it is advisable to take this fact into consideration.

The increase for Kanthal A1 from $20/68°T$ to $1300/2370°T$ is 4.2 percent. To translate this into wattage reduction:

$$\frac{E^2}{R} - \frac{E^2}{R + 0.042R} = \text{wattage at } 1300/2370°T$$

EXAMPLE 14.

A circuit exerts 12.8 ohms at 240 V.

$$\frac{240^2}{12.8} - \frac{240^2}{12.8 + 0.54} = \frac{57600}{12.8} - \frac{57600}{13.4} = 4500 - 4298 =$$

202 watts loss of power, or 4.47 percent.

It can be seen from Graph 9 that the fastest rate of resistance increase is between $400/750°T$ and $900/1650°T$, slowing down (luckily for potters) between $1200/2190°T$ and $1300/2370°T$. Table 15 is given on p. 116.

There is a somewhat similar curve in the Temperature Resistance graph for SiC elements from $1150/2100°T$ upwards (see Graphs 10 and 11) around 10 percent between $1100/2010°T$ and $1300/2370°T$ and rising thereafter at a slightly more rapid rate.

SILICON-CARBIDE RODS

The electrical principles which apply to wire elements and which have already been discussed, apply to rods as well. For example, four rods connected in series, each with a resistance of 2.5 ohms will develop 5,760 watts on 240 V. Watt-loss figures must also be carefully observed. Globar (The Carborundum Company) quotes 3–7 watts per cm^2 depending on temperature and recommend the use of voltage transformers with their elements. This greatly increases the cost, but Morganite Electroheat Crystolon Hot Rods can be used straight from the mains, although at some cost in element life and temperature control. In these circumstances the loading should be as low as is practical, i.e., the rods should have a low watt-loss figure although this can be greater than for wire.

The resistance of rods will vary with temperature. Rods are rated either at their actual resistance at $800/1470°T$ or at a nominal resistance at around $1090/1995°T$. Graph 10 gives a typical curve. It will be seen that resistance is high at switch-on, dropping to below nominal between $500/930°T$ and $1000/1830°T$. This variation in resistance is likely to give a curious heating curve, shown in Graph 13. Morganite offers an equation to give the approximate value for the resistance of any element:

$$R = 0.11 \text{ ohm/cm} \times \frac{\text{Effective length (cm)}}{\text{Cross sectional area (cm}^2)}$$

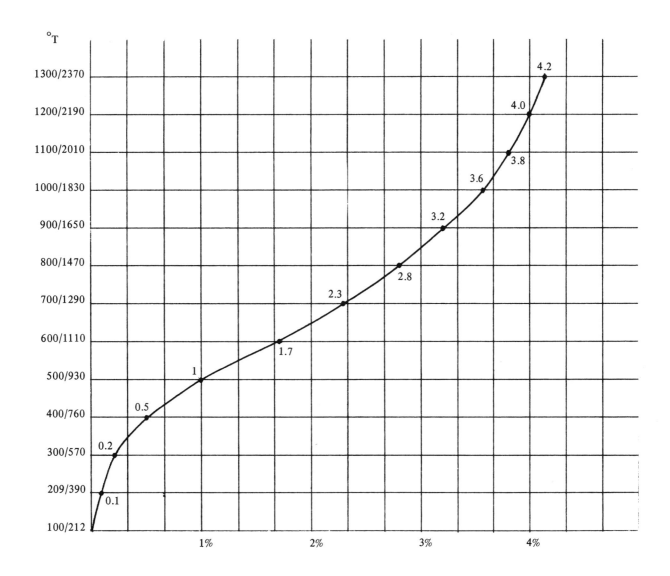

Graph 9. Increase of resistivity with temperature with consequent
power loss for Kanthal A1 wire.

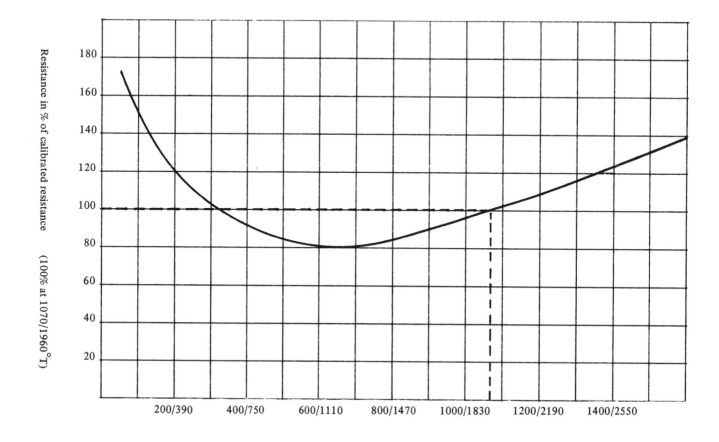

Surface temperature of rod (°T)

Graph 10. Resistance variation with temperature of Globar LL SiC rod elements.

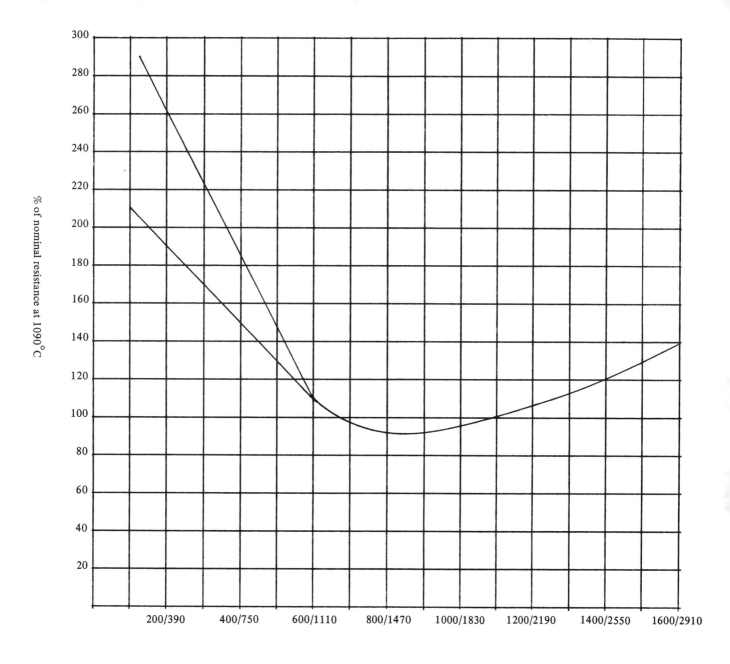

Graph 11. Resistance/temperature graph for Crystolon Hot Rods, A
Type. The converging lines at the low temperature end indicate the
range due to minor impurities in the materials.

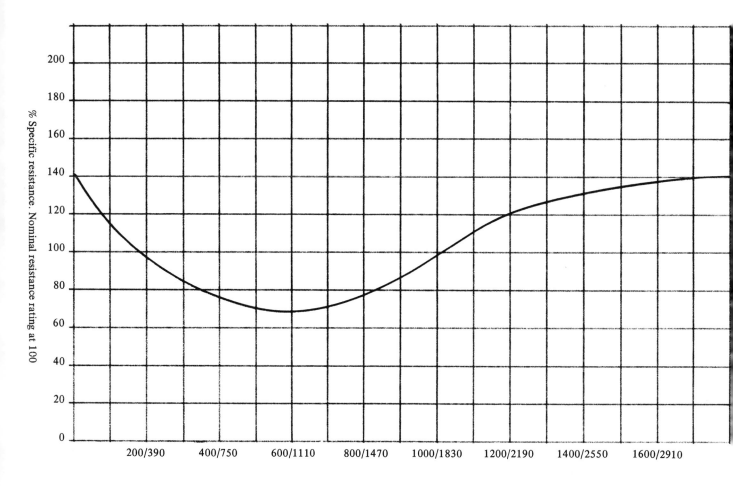

Graph 12. Resistance/temperature characteristics for Hot Line SiC
rods.

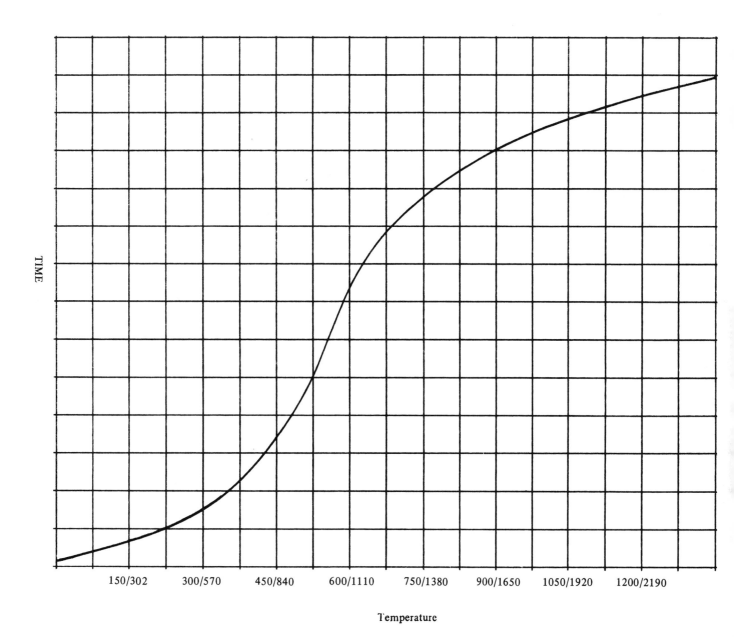

TIME

150/302 300/570 450/840 600/1110 750/1380 900/1650 1050/1920 1200/2190

Temperature

Graph 13. Approximate heating curve for SiC elements.

75

The lowest watt loading is given as 20 W/in² (twice the high-temperature maximum for wire) or 3 W/cm². Graphs 15–17 give limits for ratings above this figure. It will be noted in the Graphs that reduction lowers the maximum recommended working temperature although these graphs are concerned more with continuous-furnace and atmospheric situations rather than the intermittent conditions of pot reduction. One reason is that rods will take up carbon throughout their structure and this reduces the resistance and so increases the amount of current flowing. The carbon can be burned out by introducing oxygen (air) at periodic intervals. Water vapor should be kept to a minimum.

One of the problems of using elements in series on full voltage is that, if the resistance in one element increases, the difference between it and the others in the same circuit will tend to increase with use. Although this is seldom serious enough to jeopardize the life of the elements it is advisable to match elements plus or minus 5 percent in any series. The manufacturing tolerance is much greater than with wire and may be as much as plus or minus 20 percent (tested in air at 100 W/in²). The test voltage and current will be found on elements and cartons (Crystolon) and similar current readings indicate matching elements. The steady increase in resistance over 1100/2010°T can be allowed for by adding 10 percent to nominal resistance when high temperatures are envisaged. Table 11 gives an indication of the characteristics of some of the elements in the Crystolon range.

Three elements 0.5/12 mm × 18/455 mm would total 11.7 ohms of resistance to give about 5,000 watts. Four

such circuits in parallel could be used in an 8 ft³ kiln. Similarly, three groups of four elements 0.625/16 mm thick by 18/455 mm would give about 5,800 watts. The load however would be around 59 W/in² in the first case which is too high for 1300/2370°T according to Graph 15. The second arrangement has a loading of 40 W/in² which, although still outside the graph limits for reduction, nevertheless seems to be adequate.

Crusilite elements are glazed and are less subject to ageing or deterioration either by oxidation or reduction. The standard glaze is particularly effective for intermittent operations at all temperatures. Crusilite elements can be operated in reducing atmospheres up to about 1400/2550°T.

Rods vary considerably in their characteristics and their value to potters. The following assessments are from Peter Taylor of Labheat who can supply materials and give advice.

Hot Line Siliconit from Japan. Very good and physically strong. Contains iron which renders it self-glazing. (Offers the best results so far.)

Crusilite made in Scotland (Morganite). Very good but the cut spiral makes it very fragile in use and so not recommended for any but laboratory-size kilns.

Crystalon. "A" range not recommended but "B" range is useful, being of a dense material having a long life.

Globar (Carborundum). Has too open a texture and is not very suitable for potters.

TABLE 11

Heating Length	Diameter in/mm	Nominal Radiating Surface in²/mm²	Overall Length for 7.5/190 mm Kiln Wall	Nominal Resistance
12/305	0.44/11.1	16.49/10639	28/711	3.46
12/305	0.5/12.7	18.85/12161	28/711	2.59
18/457	0.5/12.7	28.27/18241	35/889	3.91
18/457	0.625/15.8	36.36/22802	35/889	2.48
24/610	0.625/15.8	47.14/30403	41/1041	3.32
24/610	0.75/19	56.54/36477	41/1041	2.29
30/762	0.75/19	70.68/45600	47/1194	2.88
34/864	0.75/19	80.1/51677	51/1295	3.27
36/914	1.25/31.7	141.37/91206	55/1397	1.23

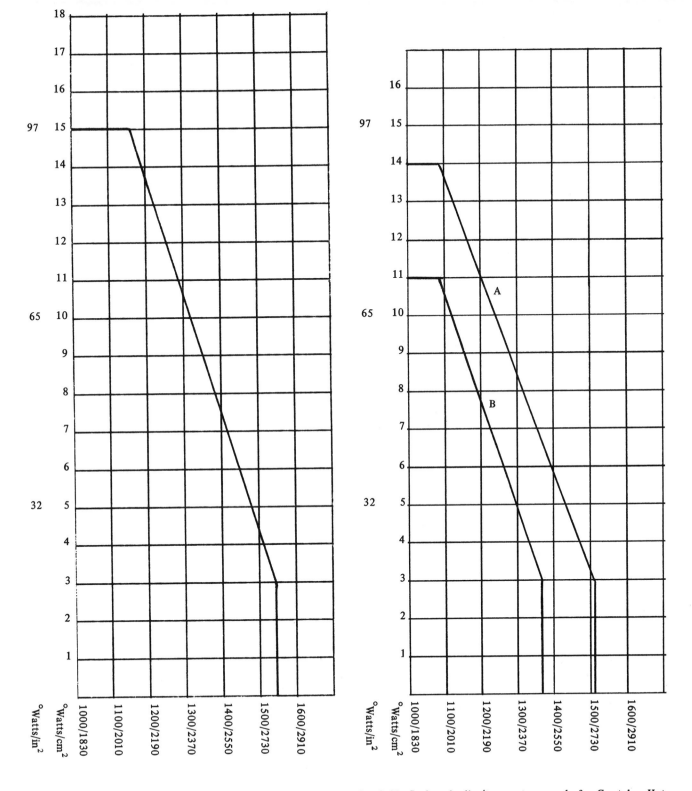

Graph 14. Surface loading/temperature graph for Crusilite rods. Maximum loading is indicated.

Graph 15. Surface loading/temperature graph for Crystolon Hot Rods. (A) Oxidizing atmosphere (B) Reducing atmosphere

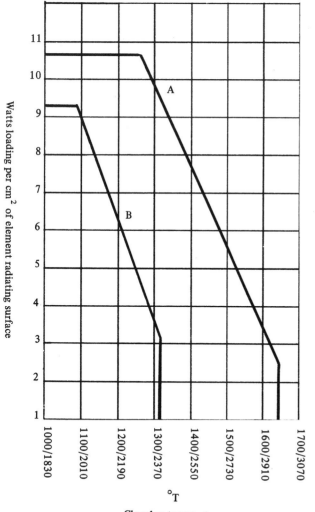

Graph 16. Surface loading/temperature graph for Globar rods. (A) air (B) reducing atmosphere. Maximum load is indicated.

Watts loading per cm² of element radiating surface

°T

Chamber temperature

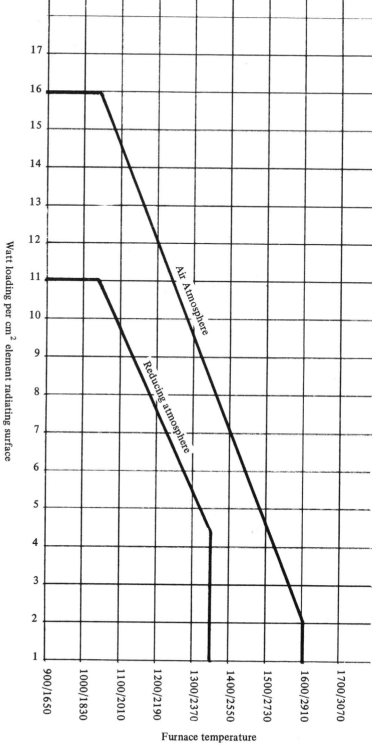

Watt loading per cm² element radiating surface

Air Atmosphere

Reducing atmosphere

Furnace temperature

Graph 17. Maximum recommended watt loading for 'Hot Line' heating rods.

DESIGN

WIRE COILS

Having arrived at the number of circuits and wire needed to power the kiln, the housing of this wire to give a balanced temperature throughout the chamber is the next consideration. As a general rule, the more the wire is dispersed, i.e., the more element slots there are, the more even the heat is likely to be (and the longer the elements are likely to last). Heat distribution is controlled by:

1. the position and spacing of the slots

2. the proportional lengths of wire in the slots, i.e., coils pulled farther apart or left closer together. It is difficult to give hard and fast rules: insulation, the shape of the chamber, etc. will affect the kiln's performance. The reasonable cost of resistance wire makes it economic to plan the elements by informed guesswork; to fire the kiln with cones or other temperature indicators at various levels; and then to alter elements if and where necessary to achieve a balanced spread of heat. As a basis for 'informed guesswork' the following notes are derived from my experience.

1. A kiln with elements in two facing walls *only* is unlikely to be fully satisfactory. At least two facing walls and floor, and preferably three or four walls should be furnished with elements. It is possible to house elements in the roof (see Diagram 51) but this is rarely done. The greater radiating surface of silicon-carbide rods appears to make a two wall and floor arrangement more acceptable.

2. The floor needs from 0.16 to 0.24 of the total power depending on the kiln proportions. The lowest wall element should be within 1.5/37 mm of the floor-bat level.

3. The upper one-third of the chamber needs more heat compared to the lower-middle section. This is due to heat loss through the roof and is especially true of top-loaders. The slots can be closer together or more tightly wound coils can be introduced. The first alternative is preferable.

As mentioned in Chapter 5 p. 56, there is an inevitable weakness in top-loaders if the top element is too near the roof-bat recess. Nevertheless the top element should be as near to the roof as is practicable.

A kiln can be planned with straight elements, hairpins, or a combination of the two. It will be realized that the current consumed by the 'tails' (the end of each coil) is virtually wasted and their number should therefore be kept to a minimum. The type and position of elements is partly controlled by the position of the mains supply in relation to the kiln: it is recommended that all mains connections be made at the same end of the kiln, or at the back in the case of front-loaders. The latter can be equipped entirely with

hairpin elements, with all the tails protruding through the back of the kiln. Any elements in the door would be carried beneath the kiln to the back in flexible metal conduit (see Illustration 47, p. 97). Top-loaders will generally need both types: mainly hairpin but with enough straights to carry all connections to one end.

If 14 swg or thinner wire is used, double hairpins will conserve energy in a small kiln by cutting the number of tails by one-third. A very simple wiring system mentioned in Chapter 5 involves long elements stretching all round the kiln, the tails emerging close together at one corner or in the middle of one side. The disadvantage of this system is that the contraction and expansion of the coils during firing will nearly always cause them to pull out of the groove at some point. This can be countered to some degree by rounding the inside corners of the kiln. See Diagram 56.

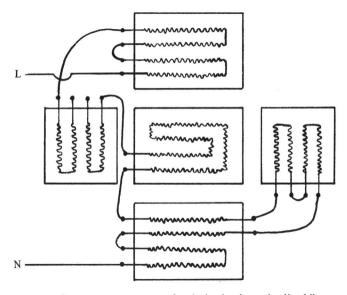

Diag. 55. Specimen arrangement of a single-circuit top-loading kiln using two straight elements to connect right-hand wall elements to the mains leads situated on the left-hand side.

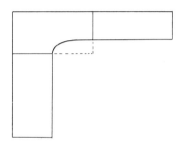

Diag. 56. Rounded corners inside kiln for all-round elements as developed by Peter Taylor (Labheat).

The elements can also be held in place at the corners and halfway along each side by means of clips of kiln wire which are pressed into small drilled holes in the brickwork. The clips soften under the full heat of the firing and are not wholly successful, though they help. It would also be possible to make corner fillets extending from top to bottom of the kiln, or to buy porcelain tubes, which will drop into holes in the kiln floor and be supported at the top with hooks of kiln wire or ceramic material. The other problem with all-round elements is that they need a very long winding rod, even if wound like hairpins in two sections, starting afresh at each end. The smaller hexagon-shaped sectional kilns may have two rows of slots to one long element, joined by a slope or 'ladder'.

Whichever system you choose, cut enough slots. This is a tedious part of the building, but, if coils are pulled well apart they will last longer, while a few spare grooves are invaluable for balancing the spread of heat in the chamber. See following section.

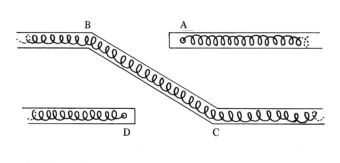

Diag. 57. A tail pierces the wall at A, the coil travels round the four walls back to B, drops to the lower slot at C, and round the kiln again to the second tail at D.

ALTERING THE ELEMENT LENGTHS

If, on firing a kiln, it is found that certain areas or levels are hotter or cooler than the main body of the chamber, it is possible to shift the heat by increasing or decreasing the element lengths. There are certain dangers in this process.

The *total wire in a circuit* controls the resistance and therefore the current flow and the power associated with that circuit. If a particular area is cooler than the rest we cannot simply add or lengthen an element to warm it up. Chapter 3 and the argument so far in this chapter make it

clear that the effect would be to increase the resistance and so cut down the *overall power* produced by the circuit.

EXAMPLE 15.
Refer back for standard circuit in Example 4.
If a 20 ft element is removed and replaced by one 28 ft long, the overall increase in the circuit length is 8 ft, bringing the total to 132 ft. The increased resistance is 8 × 0.103 (the ohms per foot of the 13 swg wire used). This equals 0.824 and raises the total resistance to 13.62 ohms. Working backwards using $P = \dfrac{E^2}{R}$, $\dfrac{240^2}{13.62} = 4228$ watts, a drop in power of 272 watts.

Conversely, by shortening an element in a hot spot, the overall power is increased. The first alteration will slow the kiln down and unbalance the circuits, if more than one, while the second may overload the wire as far as watt-loss is concerned.

A little more trouble, but a safer and more effective method, is to increase the length of one element and to shorten another *by the same amount*. This will maintain the circuit length and double the effect of heat shift. Two newly-wound elements are called for, of course; it is almost impossible to alter an element once it has been fired.

EXAMPLE 16.
If the top of a kiln is cool and the floor is too hot, it would be helpful to replace a floor element with another, say, 5/1.53 m shorter, and one at the top 5 ft longer. If the whole circuit contains 124 ft of wire this operation will result in an 8-percent heat shift.

The only limitation is that coil spacing of at least 1.25 diameters must be maintained in the longer element. An alternative which avoids the danger of too close coils is to shorten the hot-spot element and to make up the balance by introducing a new element in its own slot at the cooler level. The value of extra slots for this sort of exercise has been mentioned. In a dry-built top-loader it is a simple matter to take out the top elements, remove the top bricks, and to cut a new slot through them.

A temperature range throughout the chamber of under 10/18°T can be achieved by balancing elements in this way. A degree of correction and control can also be exercised by judicious packing. See Chapter 7.

Elements can be removed whole only if the tails run in a straight line through the wall to the connector. If tails are bent in order to reach a static connector panel (see p. 90) they will have to be broken to be removed unless they can be softened by local heating and gradually straightened.

COIL SIZES AND SPACING

The diameter and spacing of the coils will affect the efficiency and useful life of an element. There are two rules to be observed:

1. The diameter of the coil should measure 6–8 diameters of the wire. In practice this means winding 13 and 14 swg wire on a $\frac{3}{8}$/9 mm mandrel. This gives a coil of approximately 15 mm diameter. Applying the above criterion; the diameter of 13 swg is 2.33 mm; multiplied by 7 gives 16.3 mm for the average coil diameter—near enough. For thinner wires—15 to 17 swg—a $\frac{1}{4}$/6 mm winding rod gives 12 and 11 mm coils respectively, which are within the 6d–8d limits.

2. The space between one coil and the next must equal at least one wire diameter, and preferably 1.5d. A close-wound coil must therefore be stretched to two to three times its original length. It must be possible to insert a piece of the same wire between every coil and its neighbor. On the other hand, there is a limit to the degree to which one can stretch coiled wire. For 13 swg this is about a foot of wire to 5/125 mm of slot—about 7 diameters between coils.

Never attempt to lay a straight length of wire in a slot. Although this may seem a simple method of taking all connections to one end, it will expand during heating and the arc of wire will fall from its slot and may easily short circuit to the element above or below.

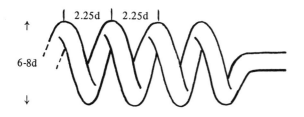

Diag. 58. The spacing must be at least 1.25d between the faces of the coils or 2.25d from topmost point of the wire to the top-most point of the next coil.

NUMBER, TYPE, AND LENGTH OF ELEMENTS

The number of slots in the kiln walls represents the number of stretched lengths of coil it can house. When coils run straight through, one slot represents one element. With hairpin elements two slots represent one element. The slots are also likely to be of different lengths. Your design should keep variations to a minimum.

Make a laid-out plan of the kiln with all the slots and their measurements shown. Work out a suitable arrangement of hairpins and straights, keeping the latter to the absolute minimum. Short-wall elements in top-loaders, and back wall elements in upright kilns must terminate about $\frac{3}{4}$/19 mm from the corners of the chamber in order to avoid contact with other elements running at right-angles to them. To arrive at their useful length, therefore, 1.5/40 mm should be deducted from the length of these slots.

Calculate the total useful length of slot in inches or centimeters and divide the overall length of wire to be housed by this number. This will give you the wire for each unit of length, e.g., 6/150 mm for each 1/25 mm of slot. Multiply each slot length by this figure (using the same unit, of course) to find the wire required for that slot. Allow twice the length for hairpins. You can now cut your total length of wire into element lengths (plus allowance for 'tails' as instructed below). Check by means of the formula and Table 9 on p. 69 that the slot is at least the minimum length required for properly spaced coils. If it isn't, you need more slots.

EXAMPLE 17.

There are 14 slots to house 200 feet of wire which is to be wound into six hairpins and two straights. Eight of the slots are 30 in long and six are 20 in. From the 20 in we deduct $1\frac{1}{2}$ in leaving a useful $18\frac{1}{2}$ in.

Total slot length: $(8 \times 30) + (6 \times 18\frac{1}{2}) = 351$ in.

$\frac{200}{351} = 0.57$ ft of wire per inch of slot. The 30 in + 30 in hairpins will consist of $60 \times 0.577 = 34$ feet of wire; the 30 in straights 17 ft; and the $18\frac{1}{2}$ in + $18\frac{1}{2}$ in hairpins $37 \times 0.57 = 21$ ft. We can check on our figures by making a total of all elements which should come to 200 ft: $(3 \times 34) + (2 \times 17) + (3 \times 21) = 199$ ft. Checking the figures against Table 9 p. 69 $351 \div 200 = 1.75$ inches of slot per foot which is very adequate for coil spacing.

The straight elements in this scheme could be eliminated by using double hairpins. These are difficult to fit if wire thicker than 0.08/2.05 mm is used.

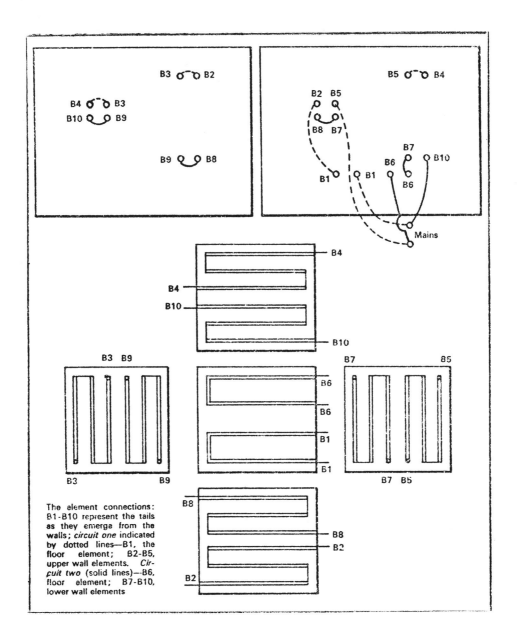

The element connections: B1-B10 represent the tails as they emerge from the walls; *circuit one* indicated by dotted lines—B1, the floor element; B2-B5, upper wall elements. *Circuit two* (solid lines)—B6, floor element; B7-B10, lower wall elements

Diag. 59. Sample double-hairpin, two circuit wiring of a top-loading kiln. The doubles obviate the use of straights.

ELEMENT TAILS

The length of the tails or leads at each end of an element should be the width of the kiln wall plus 1/25 mm if line taps are used. For static connection panels measure the required distance beyond the wall surface and add to wall thickness. For a normal kiln about 9 inches of tail is adequate and the following figures are based on this measurement.

To every element add two feet (600 mm) to allow for a 9-inch turn-back for twisting (see p. 86). The argument for two feet instead of the logical three feet (9 in $\times$ 4) is as follows: X feet of wire exerts the required resistance. $X + 2$ feet length is cut; 9 inches are folded back each end leaving $X + \frac{1}{2}$ feet. When the ends are twisted together, however, the resistance over their length is decreased—in practice by about one-third, in this case 6 inches of the total 18 inches of tails, leaving X feet of wire as the effective resistance. The degree of resistance reduction in the tails will depend on the effectiveness and closeness of the twisting. See Illustration 30.

The tails or 'cold ends' of SiC rod elements need holes about 0.5/13 mm larger than their diameter. Table 12 is derived from a Morganite Electroheat brochure.

The holes must line up very accurately over the whole length of the element. A suitable dowelling can be used to check this. Certain elements need lead-in sleeves set in the kiln wall. The suppliers will give advice on this. Sleeves are optional for the normal straight rods.

AGEING OF ELEMENTS

While many factors including voltage drop, ambient temperature, density of pack, etc., will affect the length of time that a kiln takes to reach a given heat, it will also be noticed that there is a steady, if slow, overall increase in firing time over the life of the elements. In wire elements this is due to chemical erosion of the surface and other processes which increase electrical resistance. Other deleterious effects of firing are the sagging sideways and the increasingly uneven spacing of the coils. As the wire expands and contracts, rough groove surfaces can impede movement and lead to uneven spacing of the coils. There comes a time when one or more sections of the coils become so eroded that a burn-out occurs or the firing takes so long that it becomes uneconomical or inconvenient. Before this happens the coil condition usually becomes so visibly poor and uneven that a new start is obviously called for. It is cheaper to renew, say, $30 (£15) worth of elements than to risk several times that value of pots through kiln failure.

Firing to a maximum of 1120/2050°T, the life of elements should extend over several years; at 1270/2320°T about one hundred firings may be expected; above 1275/2325°T element life expectancy may be considerably shortened. See Graph 1 on p. 17.

It is held by some engineers that the rating of an element in W/in(cm)^2 is more important for a long life than the thickness of the wire. Kanthal, however, recommends 13 swg as the minimum for stoneware temperatures and the

TABLE 12 Hole Diameters in Kiln Walls for SiC Rods

	Element Diameter					
Kiln Wall Thickness	0.375/9.5	0.44/11.5	0.5/12.5	0.625/16	0.75/19	1/25
	Hole Diameter					
5/127 mm	0.625/16	0.625/16	0.75/19	0.875/22	1.0/25	1.25/32
6.5/165	0.625/16	0.625/16	0.75/19	0.875/22	1.0/25	1.25/32
7.5/191		0.75/19	0.75/19	0.875/22	1.0/25	1.375/35
9/228		0.75/19	0.75/19	0.825/22	1.0/25	1.375/35

best situation is probably a combination of thick wire and low watt-loss figure. Wire is protected to some degree by the natural oxidation of its surface. In Kanthal A and A1 this layer is composed mainly of alumina, Al_2O_3. This can be destroyed by reduction with carbon-monoxide but is less affected by hydrogen or cracked ammonia (a mixture of hydrogen and nitrogen). For more information on this subject see Chapter 8. Any attempt at reduction should be followed by two or more oxidized firings to at least 1100/2010°T. This will re-form the surface coating but the wire will become fractionally thinner in the process.

Silicon-carbide rods are also subject to a steady increase in resistance but do not suffer to the same degree as wire from reduction. They have a long life and, like Bernard Shaw's Supermen, they die from accident more often than old age.

To counteract the slowing down of firings in a bar kiln, Peter Taylor has devised a scheme based on twelve elements. They are first connected as three circuits of four elements each. When firing time has increased by about 10 percent, they are reconnected as four circuits of three each. The third arrangement makes use of the delta system of three-phase wiring, giving three circuits of four elements each at 415 V. Lastly the wiring reverts to star with six circuits of two rods each. Multiples of twelve can be used in larger kilns.

Ill. 26. Elements of 13 swg after about 80 firings to 1270/2320°T and approaching the time when a burnout may occur.

ELEMENT FAILURE

The hum that is heard as soon as wire-element kilns are switched on is normal with Kanthal wire which is magnetic up to red heat after which sound ceases. This hum is not to be confused with any loose shaking noise which may indicate a loose connection and should be investigated. Similarly any circuit noise at higher temperatures will suggest something is wrong.

The electrical insulation value of materials will vary with temperature. Bricks are classified as insulators, but, at very high temperatures, their insulation value drops considerably. This will not cause shock to the operator of the kiln but may lead to some electrical 'leak' between one element and another when failure and consequent arcing, which momentarily raises local temperature to 2000/3650°T or more, occurs. The result is a deep, molten hole in the brick and sometimes an adjacent element may be affected. All trace of the molten material must be dug out. A plug of similar quality brick may be cut to fill the hole.

On a sophisticated installation, pilot lights or other indicators will immediately let you know of any failure during firing. Pilot lights can be a snare: they themselves may fail. Replace with a new one, or one that has remained alight, to check.

In firing a kiln with a simple supply through an isolator, the first signs of a fault may be a slowing up of the rate of temperature climb (multicircuit kilns) or a drop (single-circuit). Check that the mains supply is still operating by switching on a light or other equipment on that supply. If you suspect trouble you can *look at the company meter*. If a single-circuit kiln has failed, the disc on the meter will have ceased rotating. If the meter supplies household or workshop as well, turn off other equipment: you will probably notice a considerable slowing down of the disc rotation anyhow. For multicircuit kilns, check the readings after a fifteen- or thirty-minute period. The units registered should correspond to one-quarter or one-half the rated consumption respectively of your kiln, e.g., a 16 kW kiln should be using 4 units per 15 minutes. A small drop—say to 7 units in 30 minutes for a 16 kW kiln (up to about 10-percent drop) may be due to element aging or a mains voltage drop. Any excessive voltage drop (called a 'brown-out' in the U.S.) will also be obvious in dimmed lights, etc. If the reading has dropped 50 percent or more for a two-circuit kiln or by 33 percent for three circuits, then you can be sure that a fault has occurred in the kiln wiring, probably a burnt out element.

Check the fuses, although these are unlikely to have failed without a fault elsewhere. A kiln with three or fewer circuits, unless it is very highly powered compared with its volume, is unlikely to reach stoneware temperatures with a burnt-out element. It may limp up to 1100/2010°T or so for earthenware or to biscuit. If you plot a graph over three hours or so you can see its probable equilibrium point. (See Graph 6, p.45).

If the fault is inside the kiln, it is best to write the firing off. If the remaining elements in the circuit are reconnected they will probably burn out again because of the increased current (lower resistance) flowing through them. Needless to say, before any check is made on the kiln itself, *the kiln must be fully isolated at the mains switch.*

Having switched the kiln off, the covers can be removed from the connectors. All wire and metal will be very hot if the kiln is well under way, so approach with care and use fire-proof gloves and pliers. Any break in the connecting wires or tails may be obvious or can be detected by moving them gently. A fault is most likely to occur close to a connector. Replace broken or very corroded connecting wires. If an element tail has burnt, remove the connector and try to grip the end of the tail with long-nosed pliers and pull *gently*. If the wire is red-hot it will be quite soft and an inch or so can be pulled clear of the wall. Reconnect, *replace cover securely*, and switch on.

In the case of an internal element failure it is possible to build (previous to any emergency, of course) an insulated box—in effect a small kiln—with a single element enclosed. It must be built with proper connections and covers, and a heat-proof cable lead. If you can detect the burnt element in the main kiln by means of a battery, lamp, and leads (car jump-leads are useful), the terminals can be reconnected to the emergency 'kiln' and this should complete the circuit with just one element missing from the kiln. Replace covers and check that all leads are insulated before turning on the mains. However, the heat loss during such an operation and the necessity for providing a fully insulated and *earthed* single element 'kiln' makes this exercise of doubtful value.

Burn-outs will occur most often at the peak of a firing and may not, in fact, be noticed. It is good practice to look at your elements between firings and to check them at the beginning of each firing. As mentioned above it is cheaper to replace elements when they look worn out than to lose a kiln-load of pots. A very crude, temporary repair can be made (when the kiln is cold, of course) by looping two or three coils together, but this is unlikely to hold for long or at high temperatures. Wire can be welded with an oxyacetylene flame and a flux (borax), or by electric welding. Kan-

thal recommend the latter, without the use of a flux.

The most common, but aggravating, minor element fault is its habit of creeping out of the groove and hanging down. This should be put right as soon as it is first noticed. Heat the element to red-heat by switching it on; switch off; while the coil is still hot ease it back into place with pliers, nipping the coils a little closer together wherever the fault has occurred or looks likely to happen.

When a silicon-carbide rod fails it is usually through an accidental blow or other stress: like wire, it becomes very brittle with use. A single element in series should be replaced with a similar *used* element. If no used rod is available the group (circuit) can be discarded entirely and set aside for future used-element replacements.

It is possible, using great care, to withdraw a failed rod during firing and to replace it. This is a difficult and somewhat hazardous operation and it would depend on the value of the pack and the state of firing as to whether it would be worth the trouble.

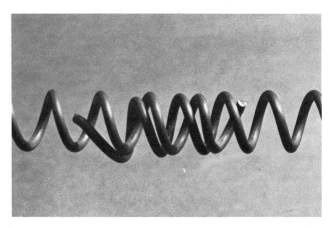

Ill. 27. A crude and temporary type of repair to a broken or burnt element. Welding would make the method more permanent.

ELEMENT WINDING

Resistance wire up to about 0.095/2.4 mm in diameter—this includes 13 swg and 11 awg—can be easily wound into coils by hand. The winder is simply a length of iron rod, $\frac{1}{4}$/6 mm or $\frac{3}{8}$/9 mm diameter (see Illustrations 30 and 35) which is bent into a handle at one end and set in two bearings. The latter can be merely two holes in $\frac{3}{4}$/20 mm thick timber.

The length of the frame depends on the maximum proposed element length when tightly wound. The bearings, will need to be about 6/150 mm farther apart than this. As a guide, 17/5 m of 13 swg will wind into about 14/350 mm of close coils. A reasonable distance between bearings, therefore is 20/510 mm. Some means of gripping one end of the wire must be provided and it must be possible to slide the completed coil from the rod. Illustrations 30–38 show one system, which I have found easy and quick. Other types of winder have been devised: the utilization of an old wallpaper trimmer by Tony Benham, for instance.

During the winding, the wire must be kept taut by feeding it through a V slot in a wood block which runs along a second shaft. Single and hairpin elements can be wound on this device at the rate of a dozen or so an hour.

To wind coils, cut the wire to the appropriate length, leaving enough for doubled tails at each end. The tails can be twisted in a vice before winding starts. Always use *wooden jaws* in the vice and take extreme care not to nip, score, or damage the wire with metal tools during any process—the wire will be only as strong as its weakest part. Wind at a regular speed and keep the coils touching one another. Perfect elements will come with a little practice. Remove the coil from the rod, grip one end in a vice and the other with pliers or both hands, and pull it steadily apart until it is stretched to the length of the slot in which it is to be housed. More professional windings can be made on a screw-cutting lathe. In this case the coils need not be close together. If the lathe bed is long enough the element can be wound to the optimum spacing for the slot into which it is to be fitted.

Hairpin elements can be wound separately from either end or, if the winder is long enough, a small block of wood can be slipped under the wire at the appropriate point and the winding continued beyond it. This process is essential for double hairpins.

Ill. 28. Element winder.

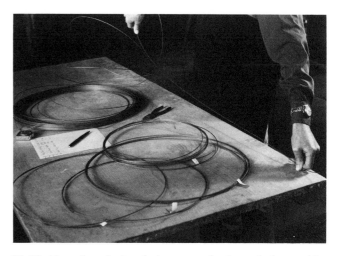

Ill. 29. Measuring wire lengths by means of units marked on a table-top. In the front of the picture are measured coils *carefully labelled* with their length, position, and type (hairpin, etc.).

Ill. 30. Twisting doubled-back tails by gripping the element end in the *wooden* jaws of a vise and holding the bent-over end with pliers or in the jaws of a brace.

The winding of 13 swg or 11 awg wire needs fairly strong wrists and a good grip. The use of an effective feed slot will help but if you doubt your ability to handle these gauges, design your kiln for one gauge thinner which, although only 13-percent smaller, takes much less effort to wind. Resistance wire is sold by weight. The length of any gauge per lb/kilo can be found at the end of this book in Table 14. One can weigh an element, new or old, to arrive at its cost or the cost of a replacement.

Ill. 33. Removing the winding bar from the bearings.

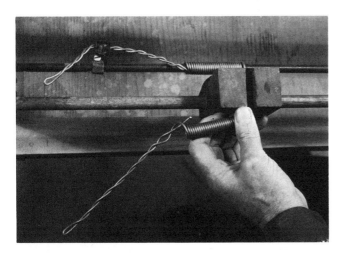

Ill. 31. The last turn of a hairpin element. The lower coil was wound separately from the other end.

Ill. 32. Winding a double hairpin. The wooden block is introduced during the winding. The completed element, with sections of different lengths to balance the heat in the kiln, is shown in Illustration 5.

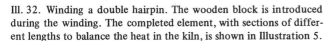

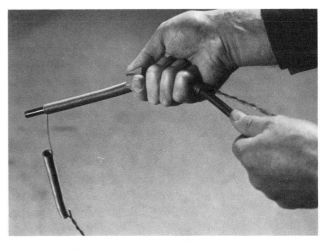

Ill. 34. The double hairpin shown in Ill. 32 is being removed from the winder rod by passing it over the handle.

Ill. 35. One twisted tail is gripped in the wooden jaws of a vise while the other is pulled firmly by hand with a mole wrench. The coil will spring back to some degree when released. The table or a length of wood can be marked with units of length to serve as a length guide.

SILICON-CARBIDE RODS

It is not practical, financially and technically to distribute rod elements over the walls of a kiln as completely as one can with wire. The fact that they are freestanding and have a greater radiating surface partly balances this limitation. Two walls or two walls and floor are the normal positions for rods. With vertical mounting the back wall of a front-loading kiln could also be furnished with elements.

The electrical considerations have been dealt with in Part I of this chapter, and connections, etc., under the appropriate sections.

Rods are self-supporting if chosen for their location. Recommendations by Peter Taylor are:

Up to 32/813 mm   span rods should be 14 mm diameter
Up to 39/991 mm   span rods should be 16 mm diameter
Up to 50/1270 mm span rods should be 18 mm diameter

These are minimum requirements. Under no circumstances should any part of the hot central section of the rod be contained within the wall of the kiln.

Normally each element consists of a single straight rod and this poses problems when designing an upright, front-opening kiln. The connections are necessarily in close proximity to the door opening and the shielding forms a rather deep recess when added to the wall thickness. This is more a hindrance to easy packing in a small kiln than in a large one since the depth of the recess will be similar in each case. There is no such problem in top-loader design.

A hairpin type of SiC element is made which would obviate the design difficulties. Using these elements, you can make all connections at the back of the kiln or can suspend them from the roof. These elements are, however, expensive.

Ill. 36. A silicon-carbide-element kiln with the rods mounted vertically. These are Japanese "Hot Line" rods and have been used under reducing conditions for four years without replacement. (Photo courtesy Labheat)

SiC rods may also be mounted vertically with the connections in the roof and floor of the kiln. SiC rods may also be mounted vertically with the connections in the roof and floor of the kiln. The rod should rest on an insulator, such as a strip of Sindanyo, at its lower end, though some are made with a suspending pin. The space between rod and exit hole should be lightly packed with asbestos or ceramic fiber to prevent a 'chimney effect' from developing

Using their standard group of twelve elements (see p. 84), Labheat also devised a trolley kiln which uses space economically, permits loading on one-half of a truck while the other is firing, and requires no doors. Diagram 62 and Illustrations 37 and 38 show the principle on which it is built and the extreme simplicity of the interior arrangements. The door and back wall are actually built onto the truck. Careful measurement and building of the brickwork is essential. Trucks are, apparently, available as rejects from industrial continuous-tunnel kilns. The chamber is similar to that shown in the specifications for Kiln 4 at the end of this book but on a larger scale and without a floor.

Diag. 60. The walls can be cut with shallow grooves as shown so that the rods need not protrude far into the chamber. Recommended clearances are shown. Distance from any part of rod to wall should be at least $0.5d$, with a minimum of $1.5d$ between rods.

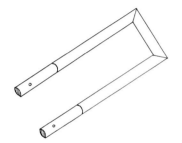

Diag. 61. Hairpin type of SiC element.

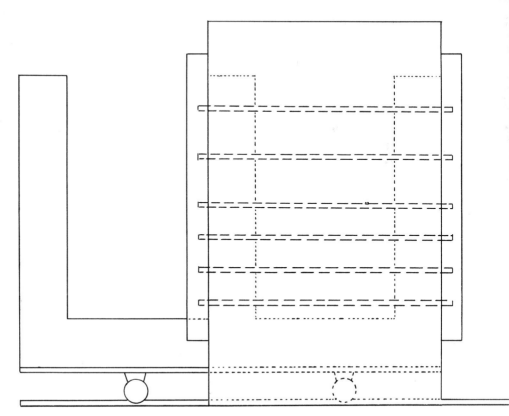

Diag. 62. A general impression of the Labheat trolley kiln, with one loaded section firing in the chamber.

Ill. 37. The interior of the kiln with six stout rods in each wall. The brick wall facing the camera is attached to the trolley and not to the chamber, and travels through the chamber length each time the truck is moved. (Photo courtesy Labheat)

CONNECTORS

Elements in series are connected one to another on the outside of the kiln wall. Steam and gases given off during firing, plus considerable heat, attack terminals and connectors which must be resistant to these hazards. The ceramic-cased brass or copper connectors normally used for lower temperature work will rapidly oxidize and arc or break down as a result of any series of firings above about 1000/1830°T. The plastic-cased connectors are, of course, quite useless. It is difficult to move screws once they have started to blacken, and only equipment which can be tightened and loosened by means of spanners is likely to stand the strain. There are two systems of connection for wire elements:

1. A strip of metal or Sindanyo asbestos on which all the connections are located. If the connectors are located on metal, porcelain insulators must be used; if asbestos is used the nuts can tighten straight onto the strip. This system is advantageous because it is tight, tidy, and space-saving. It is only practicable, however, where the element tails pierce the wall in straight rows. Its main disadvantage is that the tails often have to be bent towards the connectors, necessitating extra length and making the removal of an element in one piece virtually impossible. It also imposes more rigidity on the design and makes additions or alterations difficult. If you design a kiln with this type of connection make sure that the tails are long enough to reach the studding and loop round it.

2. A more flexible method is to make connections between a tail and a length of asbestos-covered wire by means of a line tap. Most of the wall space may be involved and the system requires much more extensive casing than the previous one. However the casing can be built into the kiln frame and does not impose serious problems. Line taps are not often available from ordinary retail shops but your electrician can buy them from wholesalers, or they might be obtainable through your local electricity supply company. Line taps, which are used to connect mains cables, are made in various sizes. The size and type shown in Illustration 40 is suitable for wire-element work. The surface of the tap is 'sherardized', a special zinc plating on steel, which inhibits corrosion. They are tightened and loosened with spanners as in Illustration 41.

Ill. 38. One of the trolley packs being wheeled out of the chamber after a firing. The packed but unfired ware on the other half of the trolley is now in the chamber, entering from the far end. Note the heat-seal ledge of bricks which runs in a groove at the base of the chamber. An explanation of the 'pillars' on each side of the chamber will be found in Specification 4 p. 137. (Photo courtesy Labheat).

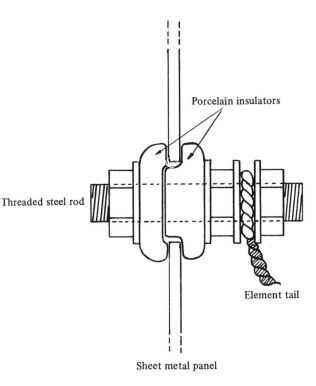

Porcelain insulators

Threaded steel rod

Element tail

Sheet metal panel

Diag. 63. Section through porcelain insulators which prevent threaded metal rod from contacting the metal panel onto which the connections are fitted.

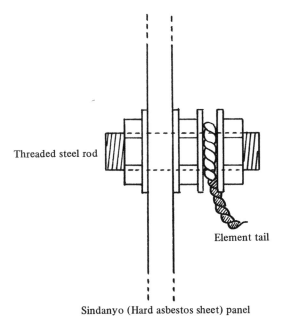

Threaded steel rod

Element tail

Sindanyo (Hard asbestos sheet) panel

Diag. 64. Similar section through connection on Sindanyo or other insulating panel.

Ill. 39. Ceramic-cased brass connectors suitable for low temperature work only (raku, enamels, etc.).

Ill. 40. A sherardized line tap. A suitable size for potters has a slot $\frac{5}{8}$/15 mm long; the body of the tap is of a similar diameter.

91

For high temperature kilns the *copper wires* connecting the elements through the line taps should be covered with woven asbestos. This is now black in color and gummy in texture to prevent the asbestos from flying about in the air. There are other heat-resistant wire coverings on the market but they have a ceiling of about 120/250°T and are likely to decompose under repeated firings. At one time wire would be threaded through ceramic 'beads' usually of porcelaneous material and it would be quite easy for the potter to repeat this system. The gauge of wire must be suitable for the load on the circuit in which it is used. See Chapter 7, p. 114 for Table 13 of wire sizes.

Silicon-carbide rods are connected by means of braided terminal straps held in place with a clamp. There must be slack at the terminal strap connections to allow for slight twisting of the rod and clearance between the outside wall and the clamps so that elements are free to expand and contract, and so that the expansion of the kiln itself during heating cannot place the rods under tension.

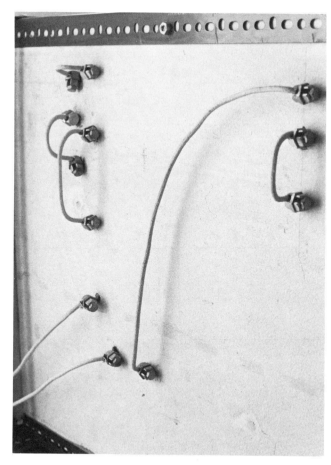

Ill. 42. Connections using line taps and asbestos-covered wire.

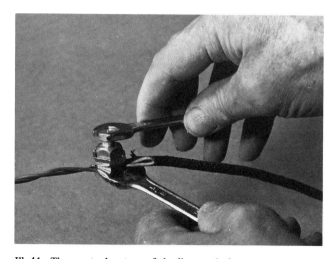

Ill. 41. The great advantage of the line tap is that two spanners can be used on it as shown here. This not only ensures a tight connection but also makes it easy to undo, even if corroded, without breaking a brittle element tail.

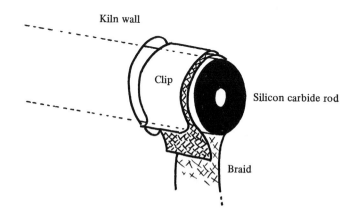

Diag. 65. SiC rod braid and clamp connection. The clamp may take one of a number of forms, e.g., it may be opened like a spring clip.

7. Installation

The installation of electrical supply as far as the isolating switch (no. 7 in Diagram 66) is usually a job for the professional electrical engineer or your electricity supplier. If you do any of the work yourself, have it checked professionally—and study a good manual on wiring first. However, it is useful for the potter to know what is necessary to be able to recognize the components of an installation, and to be able to diagnose (and in the case of fuses, for example, put right) faults as they occur. An efficiently wired system should give no trouble over many years of use. Diagram 66 shows the *maximum* set of equipment that may be found in connection with a supply which involves special rates and limitations of supply to certain times, or periods of the year. If you are on a straight all-times rate in England, then items 1, 4, 4a, and 5 would be eliminated. Many electric companies do not use 3A, and not all, 4a.

Diag. 66. Diagrammatical layout of the *maximum* electrical installation. (1) switch (2) fuse (3) meter (3A) earth leakage circuit breaker (4) time switch clock (4A) contactor isolating switch (5) contactor (6) fused switch (6A) change-over switches (7) kiln isolating switch (8) kiln

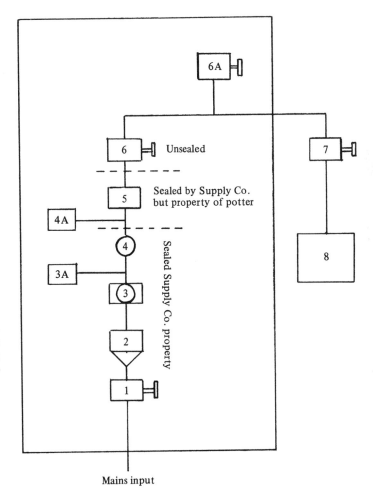

The components shown on Diagram 66 are as follows:

1. A sealed *switch* on the electric company's side of mains fuses. This is not used in Great Britain on small to medium installations but is sometimes called for in the U.S. and other countries.

2. Sealed *fuses* to protect the main feed cables against overloading. Only a serious short circuit or overload which somehow managed to bypass the switch-fuses could affect these.

Ill. 43. A typical installation (in Great Britain). Reading from top left to bottom right: time clock; meter; earth-leakage circuit breaker; (switch not connected with kiln installation); fused switch box—three phase; contactor insolating switch; contactor.

3. The *meter* must be rated to deal with the maximum supply you intend to draw from the whole system. The electric company must be consulted on this matter or serious damage could occur. The meter will register watts used per hour—watt-hours. One thousand watts for one hour (kWh) constitutes one unit of electricity supplied, the usual basis for charging for electricity.

3A. An *earth leakage circuit breaker* (ELCB), often known as an Earth Trip, operates a multipole switch which will isolate the installation from the supply in the event of an earth fault. It will occasionally operate for no apparent reason. It can be reset by the consumer but will fail to complete the circuit if the fault is still operating. A press-button is incorporated by which the consumer can test the continuing effectiveness of the device.

4. The *time switch clock* can be a very involved piece of mechanism with hourly, daily, or monthly cycles, or all three. It operates a small switch which can carry enough current to energize the electromagnets of the contactor. On some systems it may operate a switch-over from one recording dial to another in the meter, or may alter the rate at which units are charged.

4A. The clock will control the contactor, but the latter may fail or develop a fault. In order to handle the workings of the contactor the supply must be switched off. The company could do this by removing their fuses (2) but some electric companies require an *isolating switch* between the mains and the contactor for this purpose.

5. The circuit is opened and closed through the *contactor* by the operation of springs (to open) and electromagnets (to close). If the time switch clock fails to energize the magnets, no current is available for the kiln. In the event of supply failure one can check the contactor by means of the isolator (4A) or the ELCB (3A) if either are fitted. When these are switched on and off you should be able to hear the contacts making and breaking the connection. If there is no sound and the supply should be available, then either the clock or the contactor may be at fault. Check that the mains current is still operating the other circuits in the pottery. In any case you will need to call the electric company.

6. The *fused switch* is the first piece of equipment in the series over which the potter has control. The fuses should be just strong enough to carry the load.

6A. If you have more than one kiln the wiring which would be necessary for supplying current to all at once might prove very costly. A special *change-over switch* can be fitted which makes it impossible to run two kilns at the same time; it takes but a moment to switch the supply from one kiln to the other or to isolate both from the mains. In this case the mains wiring, contactor, meter, etc., need be of a caliber to supply only the larger of the kilns. This is especially valuable on a maximum-load charge when running both kilns together for half an hour can double your standing charge. The change-over-switch system can be extended to cover any number of kilns or other apparatus. It must be stressed that no kiln or group of kilns taken from any one circuit should be powered to exceed the input rating.

Ill. 45. A three-phase (or two- or three-circuit, single-phase) fused switch box. Note neutral connections at top left. More modern switches may use a "cartridge" fuse. The switch handle is obscured by the hand. This type of switch is on when the handle is hanging vertically downwards and off when standing out horizontally (opposite to light switches!). The case can be opened only when switched off.

Ill. 44. The contactor with cover removed. The upright bars are drawn inwards when the electromagnets are energized (by a time switch or by an energy regulator). Three-phase and neutral wiring is used in this instance, all four poles make and break the circuit.

Ill. 46, A two-way change-over switch with cover removed. The contactor blades are standing out horizontally and all circuits are off. When handle is pressed downward the blades connect three circuits; when pressed upward, three different circuits.

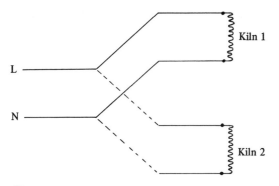

Diag. 67. A simple single-phase two-way system using two-pole switching of line and neutral.

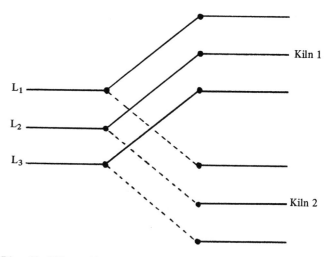

Diag. 68. This could represent a three-phase system, or three circuits or groups of circuits from a single phase. The kilns connected as continuous lines in diagram would be powered when the switch position is upwards, those on the dotted lines, when switch is downwards. The lines would, of course, be wired back to a shared neutral (not shown).

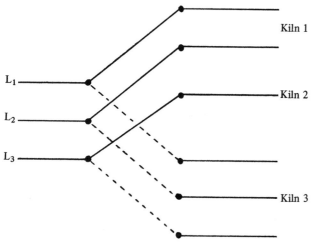

Diag. 69. This system is similar to Diagram 65 but with two smaller kilns taken from the upper position and a large one from the lower. The sum of the upper kilns cannot exceed the rated input.

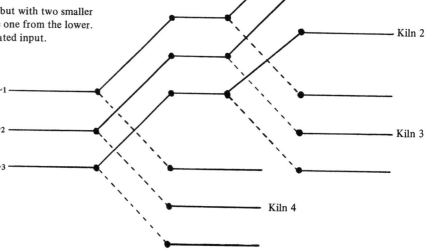

Diag. 70. Indefinite extension of system ensuring that only one maximum load is connected at any one time.

7. The main group of components 1–6 can be mounted on a board near the supply input. Your kiln may or may not be in the same room. An *isolating switch* immediately adjacent to the kiln is essential for two reasons: to break the circuit conveniently when firing, or immediately in the case of a fault; and to act as a connecting box between the leads from the kiln and those from the supply board. There may be some loss of voltage on a long cable between board and kiln and the ideal site is about 7/2 m apart. This may, of course, be through the floor to a lower level.

This completes the installation as far as the supply of current is concerned but the control of temperature rise may involve a second contactor. See Chapter 8.

Ill. 47. The isolating switch next to the kiln with flexible conduit used to house the wires from switch to kiln. The frog is the Fournier kiln god!

WIRING

The connections 2–4 in Diagram 63 are usually carried on separate double-insulated type wires which may well be uncased. The time-switch and contactor may be similarly connected or, if an isolating switch (4A) is fitted, the wiring can be housed in a box or length of 'trunking' as in Illustration 43. From the fused switch (6) to the kiln isolator, single-phase wiring can be of the multiple-cable type with two cores and earth wire encased in a single P.V.C. sheath. Three phases, however, are carried on separate wires and these should be protected by running them in tough plastic or metal tubing (conduit) which is fastened to the wall with screwed clips. From isolator to kiln, flexible metal conduit (see Illustration 47) is normally used, with fittings at each end to anchor it to the switch box and the kiln casing. It is advisable to use this type of conduit for single- and three-phase supplies between switch and kiln. Depending upon the type of flexible conduit used, an earth continuity conductor (earth wire) may be required to be run with the supply cables, and to be connected to the frame (metalwork) of the kiln. Check with your supplier. The wires from the elements to the isolator (or to a junction box in the casing of the kiln) should be asbestos covered.

All wiring must be able to conduct the maximum *current* you will require without overheating. For a similar load in watts the current will vary with the voltage: $I = \dfrac{P}{E}$

EXAMPLE 1.

$I = \dfrac{4000}{240} = 16.6$ amperes

$I = \dfrac{4000}{110} = 36.6$ amperes

To take 4 kW, therefore, the feed wires for 110 V supply must be of more than twice the cross-sectional area compared with the same load on a 240 V supply.

It is useful, on a three-phase supply, to be able to identify the phases at any point. They can be labelled with colored tapes (standard colors are red, yellow, and blue) or as A, B, C at the input point, on the switch-fuse, and at the kiln isolating switch. One or more circuits of elements can be isolated by withdrawing the appropriate fuse.

In the U.K. the use of plugs and sockets for connecting electric apparatus is not commonly used for loads over 13 A although industrial plugs and sockets are available for three-phase and single-phase 60 A plus, at mains voltage. In the U.S. many of the smaller kilns are wired for plugs and receptacles up to 50 A, 250 V loading. Diagram 68 is derived from M. Wikey's *Calibrating the Electric Kiln.*

EARTHING OR GROUNDING

The different electrical terms used in the U.K. and the U.S. and the variety of legal prohibitions can cause confusion. In the U.K. the wires used to complete a circuit are called 'line' and 'neutral.' The neutral is provided by the electricity supply authority and has blue or black insulation. It is not normally used as an 'earthing' wire. In the U.S. the term is 'grounded neutral' and the insulation is white: in interior wiring systems black insulation is used on an *ungrounded* conductor. In neither country is the neutral wire carried through a fuse. The 'line' or 'live wire' in the U.K. is a 'hot lead' in the U.S.

The American 'ground wire' which connects the service switch to earth is known in the U.K. as the 'earthing lead' while the 'grounding wire' which runs with the current carrying wires and connects all metal objects which may accidentally come into contact with the hot lead is equivalent to the 'earth continuity conductor.' The whole system is colloquially known as the 'earth' or 'earth wire'.

It is essential, under all conditions, that metal conduit, switches, the casing of the kiln, etc., be earthed or grounded efficiently so that any leakage of current is immediately short-circuited, thus melting the fuse or disconnecting the supply through the ELCB.

When grounding the casing of the kiln some problems arise if the metal angle is supplied *painted* before assembly. One can make contact at the joints by cutting through to the metal, with a rough file, under the nut and bolt head. Two or three earthing connections can also be made to vulnerable metal frame members, filing away any non-metallic coating and using a bolt for good contact.

The earth wire may be incorporated in the cable or can be run as a separate conductor. In the U.S., when two 120 V hot leads are used to provide a 240 V supply, the grounded neutral is connected to the casing of the kiln and installation.

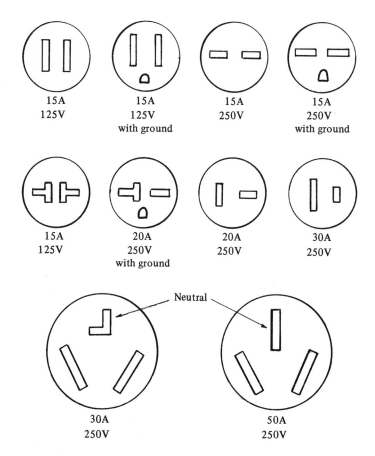

Diag. 71. Some U.S. plug receptacles. (Reproduced by kind permission of M. Wikey)

Some other terms which are not synonymous in the two countries are:

U.S.	U.K.
raceway	conduit or trunking
isolating switch (not designed to open circuit on load)	isolating switch (usually a load-carrying switch)
attachment plug	plug top
receptable	socket outlet
wye system (three phase)	star system

SAFETY SWITCHES

There are a number of switches on the market operated by means of a plunger which is so sprung that, without continuous pressure being applied, it is always at the off position. Such a switch can be mounted on the front of a kiln so that the door frame, or an arm extended from it, will depress the switch to on only when the door is firmly shut. It is more difficult to operate a safety switch on a top-loader, although one could be operated by a lid hinged as in Diagram 34.

Since the kiln cannot be switched on unless firmly closed up, a loose roof brick or other ventilation system must be incorporated. In a situation where there are children or where there is a danger of kilns being accidentally switched on, the use of a safety switch is very desirable.

For small kilns the current can be controlled through the switch itself but for loads of about 5 kW and upwards, or for multiphase installations, the switch operates a contactor (see Chapter 7, Illustration 44) which actually makes and breaks the circuit to the kiln.

8. Temperature Controls and Indicators

Kiln controls are like hi-fi equipment: beyond a certain fairly simple level they are subject to diminishing returns on capital outlay and become more liable to malfunction. I work to the extreme of austerity with a switch and a cone but make no virtue of this!

PYROSCOPES

There are two main groups of heat indicators: pyroscopes and pyrometers. The most widely used are the pyrometric cones. They are heat-work indicators and are usually very reliable and consistent so long as their seating, slope, and positioning are kept constant. Suppliers, for obvious reasons, recommend three cones per firing: for warning, optimum, and overfire. One cone, however is quite sufficient if you are sure to be on hand at the critical period (and a dozen cones would be useless if you are not!). Even with a single cone there is a twenty- to thirty-minute warning from the first signs of bending to touchdown. These remarks refer to electric kilns; the firing of fueled kilns in reduction may pose different problems.

Cones are given specific 'squatting' temperatures but the precise firing speed and degree of curve which corresponds to this temperature is always in some doubt. In practice a certain 'reference point' should be decided upon: either the first sign of cone movement, a visible degree of bend, or the cone point touching the shelf on which it is set. The cone tip touching down is a fairly precise reference so long as the slope and setting can be kept standard. If a higher temperature is required than this point indicates, a subsequent period of firing can be set on a kitchen 'timer' clock, the period decided upon through the experience of several firings and results.

The placing of the cone vis-à-vis the spyhole, the elements, and the pack can affect the cone's performance. It can be as close as 1.5/40 mm to the spyhole; if farther than about 5/125 mm it will be difficult to see at temperatures above 1250/2280°T. If the cone begins to merge with its background, it can be brought momentarily into darker relief by blowing gently into the spyhole. Beware singeing whiskers or eyebrows. As mentioned before, the slope is critical, and a card or pottery tile can be cut to check this. Orton specifies 8 degrees from the upright but in my experience 15 degrees is more practical. The whole of the cone need not be visible at the start of the firing but it should be so arranged as to fall into full view as it bends. Never sacrifice cone placing to the packing in of that extra pot.

Ill. 48. The touch-down reference point for "cone control."

Cones measure heat-work rather than temperature. Scales of equivalents are often given, dependent on certain speeds of temperature rise. Speeds from 60/140°T to 240/465°T an hour are mentioned, none of them very useful in a practical way since the temperature curve always shows an ever-decreasing rate of climb. It is said that the faster the firing, the higher the actual temperature will be at which the cone melts, with a possible variation of 25/45°T. In my experience, however, the differences in glaze color and texture between firings using the same number cone in the same way but which vary in heating time between seven and twelve hours is small and may be attributed to the longer fire rather than resulting from variations in the end-temperature. Cones are, after all, glazes in a special form. It is advisable to buy cones in boxes of one hundred to ensure a degree of consistency, and to check for any difference between one box and another by comparisons in the same kiln. Staffs cones with the number prefaced by the letter H will differ from those that do not. Cones are made in two sizes: standard $2\frac{1}{2}$/63 mm long, and miniature or Junior. Orton Junior cones are pressure molded, physically stronger, and used especially for 'kiln sitters' where the bending of the cone switches off the kiln. See p. 107.

Holdcroft Bars behave like cones, working on a similar principle but are supported at each end and sag in the middle at the appropriate temperature. Buller's Rings and glaze trial hoops need a larger spyhole for their removal (they give their information when cold) than the average electric kiln is fitted with.

PYROMETERS

In certain situations, where it is not desirable or possible to keep a check on cones, or where special and variable firing schedules are practised, a pyrometer will indicate the temperature inside the kiln—or, at least, that part of the chamber into which the thermocouple protrudes. Pyrometers offer better early-warning systems than cones both of approaching maturing temperature and of any malfunction of the kiln, and they are essential to any programmed system of firing. A thermocouple will not indicate the state of glaze-melt, nor take regard of the rate of temperature rise, both of which influence cones to some degree. This is the difference between temperature and heat-work.

The device for indicating the temperature in a kiln consists of two sections:

1. The *thermocouple* which generates a small voltage dependent on temperature.

2. The *indicator*, often called a galvanometer but actually a millivoltmeter.

The pyrometer system makes use of what is known as the Seebeck Effect. If two wires of different metals or alloys are joined at their ends to form a circuit and the two junctions maintained at different temperatures, then an electric current will flow around the circuit. The thermocouple consists of two wires fused together at the end which is measuring the temperature—the 'hot junction.' A very small voltage is set up between the wires which increases as the temperature of the junction rises. It is this voltage which is measured by the indicator. The wires of the thermocouple may be based on nickel or platinum according to the

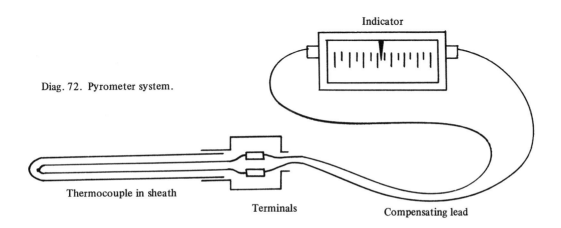

Diag. 72. Pyrometer system.

Indicator

Thermocouple in sheath

Terminals

Compensating lead

maximum operating temperature. The former may be known as type K or Chromel-Alumel (trade name) and has a 90-percent-nickel and 10-percent-chromium alloy for the positive leg, and alloy of 94-percent nickel with traces of aluminum, manganese, and silicon for the negative leg. It must not be used for firings above 1100/2010°T. The more expensive platinum-rhodium/platinum, or P/R, couple can be used at any temperature normally attained by the potter. Type K has a limited life through evaporation and diffusion; the latter is long-lasting and should remain accurate indefinitely.

In an oxidizing atmosphere it is not necessary to have a sheath over the thermocouple but one is usually provided for mechanical protection. The sheaths may be of sillimanite, mullite, fused quartz, fused alumina, or aluminous porcelain. Reduction can harm the wires and the sheath must be of impervious mullite or aluminous porcelain. The cold ends of the wires, outside the kiln, are fitted with terminals for connecting to the pyrometer indicator. It is the millivolt potential which is generated by the temperature difference between the hot and cold ends of the thermocouple which is measured by the indicator. The leads between the sections are constructed to compensate for the fact that the so-called 'cold' junction gets warmer as the firing proceeds. The compensating cable or extension lead is an extension of the thermocouple in effect, though not of the same expensive alloys: copper/copper-nickel replace the P/R and this allows the terminals in the head of the thermocouple to reach 100/210°T with negligible error as the true 'cold junction' has now been moved to the far end of the compensating cable, i.e., to the indicator terminals. It follows that the indicator should be far enough away from the kiln heat not to be unduly affected by it.

Within the indicator is a light coil of copper wire which rotates in the magnetic flux of a permanent magnet. The coil, influenced by the tiny voltage (about 14 millivolts or $\frac{1}{70}$ of a volt at 1280/2340°T), pivots on low-friction bearings or is suspended from taut bands of high-tensile alloy. A pointer fixed to the coil traverses a dial calibrated in °T. The indicator is obviously a very delicate instrument which can suffer damage in transit. The terminals should always be connected together with bare copper wire when the instrument is being moved, to prevent it swinging about. Once installed the pyrometer should give years of service without attention. The pointer should be set to read the air temperature near its terminals, or can be adjusted to read the temperature at the tip of the thermocouple which can be checked with a thermometer. There is usually a small 'zero-adjuster' button in the front face which is

turned with a screwdriver to move the pointer. Mount the indicator as fas as possible from the kiln. A pyrometer is self-powered and needs no battery or mains electrical supply.

Experience (trial and error) is the basis of all potting techniques and the use of electronic equipment is no exception. You will learn to know what your pyrometer means in terms of firing results. A frequent complaint about pyrometers is their apparent inaccuracy—indicating temperatures as much as 60/108°T above or below that which appears to be operating in the kiln. The following checks can be made on your pyrometer installation.

1. Make sure that you are using the right type of thermocouple (P/R for any temperature above 1100/2000°T).

2. The thermocouple must protrude a sufficient distance into the kiln. The sheath should have a length clear of the kiln wall of at least twice its diameter.

3. Do not site the thermocouple in a particularly hot or cool place in the kiln.

4. See that you have tight and clean connections at each end of the compensating lead.

5. Damaged or incorrectly linked wires will affect the reading. If the wires are changed over at both the indicator and thermocouple terminals and the result is a higher reading, then the new connection is correct.

6. The very fine setting of the pyrometer may have been damaged in transit. Only the supplier can remedy this.

Ill. 49. A pyrometer indicator (Photo courtesy Sifam Ltd., Torquay, England.)

7. The pyrometer should have been calibrated for maximum accuracy *within your firing range*. Check this with the supplier when ordering.

8. Choose the longest calibration scale available. Plus or minus 1-percent inaccuracy of the full scale reading can mean an error of up to 14/25°T on a 1400/2500° scale.

9. Set the ambient reading as instructed above.

10. Make sure that you are reading the pointer correctly: it should exactly cover its own reflection in the polished metal strip, generally called the 'mirror', behind it.

11. The indicator ambience should be normal room temperature—about 20/70°T. Site it therefore at least 3/1 m from the kiln and preferably farther away. If the compensating cable is too short it can be extended with ordinary copper wire provided that the temperature difference between the two ends of the copper cable is only a few degrees—up to 8/15°T.

12. Do not run compensating leads near to or parallel with mains cables, which may induce current in them and falsify readings.

If, in spite of all your care, the reading does not appear to correspond with your assumptions about the temperature within the kiln, then you must make a mental adjustment, adding or subtracting the degrees of error. A chart can be affixed above the indicator giving the indicator reading against the 'true' temperature for the firing range. If the pointer starts at room temperature, the error will be different at every stage and you may need to use cones to construct a rough graph.

SIMPLE CONTROLS

The one essential control is the on-off switch. It is possible to fire most pottery with no other help. Very large, thick-walled pieces are liable to crack or explode if heated too rapidly up to 120/250°T and for this type of production something more sophisticated may be called for. However, I have fired all thrown wares and hand-built pieces up to 20/500 mm high with a switch and a cone for the last thirty years with very little mishap. Some care and attention is needed, turning the kiln on and off to dry the wares thoroughly but apart from that the full power is applied from start to finish of the firing. Temperature controllers and energy regulators merely turn the kiln on and off at prescribed intervals.

Top-loaders can be used, during one firing, to dry the ware for the next, ensuring that no absorbed water remains in the fabric of the pots. A slow initial heating in the kiln is still needed to drive off the more tenacious adsorbed water which clings to the molecules of apparently dry clay. A

sample schedule might read: kiln on for 5 minutes, off for 10, on 5, off 20, on 15, off 20, then on for the firing. Tests, however, should be made for your special needs. If a pyrometer is used this should reach 150/300°T before the full firing starts. The kiln door or roof must be left partly open for the first hour or so (or the ventilation brick left out). If you have three-phase or separately fused circuits there is another control to hand, albeit a crude one, the fuse box. One or more fuses can be removed to decrease the overall power in the kiln although local heat may still be a danger. The method is not recommended by electricians and is rather clumsy. The same result can be obtained by wiring a switch into each circuit. If this system is envisaged it is advisable to spread the elements in each circuit as evenly through the kiln as possible.

CONTROLLING PYROMETERS

When using a cone or simple pyrometer the current must be switched off by hand when the firing temperature is reached. This can be done automatically by a controller in conjunction with a power contactor. For cone-controlled shut-off see p. 107.

INDICATING CONTROLLERS

These look like a simple pyrometer indicator with the addition of a red pointer which can be set by means of a knob to the required firing temperature. As the black pointer swings level with the red one, the kiln will either 'soak' (maintain a given temperature plus or minus a few degrees) or be switched off. In a moving-coil type of controller the indicating pointer carries a small vane which passes between a lamp and a photodetector at a given point and switches off the kiln supply. In a potentiometric controller a voltage difference between contacts on the two pointers is sufficient to hold the contactor closed until the two pointers are in line when the voltage will have fallen to zero and the contactor is allowed to open thus cutting supply to the kiln. A small disadvantage of the latter type is that the indicator is driven by a small motor which ceases to operate when the current is switched off so that the pointer will remain at the top temperature even though the kiln is cooling.

Controlling pyrometers may be fitted with a soak and/or cut-off options. If the soak is brought into use, it will continue to hold the peak temperature indefinitely and must be finally switched off by hand unless an additional piece of mechanism is connected in the form of a time-clock. This can be set to determine the length of soaking period after which current is disconnected. The two functions can be combined in one controller.

The final sophistication is a program controller which will monitor all the variations in heating and cooling of which the kiln is capable. The program of temperature against time (e.g., two hours to 100/212°T for drying; one hour at 120/250°T for driving off adsorbed water; two hours to 700/1290°T; and so on for a programmed biscuit fire) is cut on a cam which is set on a spindle which rotates it slowly, driving the red pointer upscale at the predetermined rate, the black pointer keeping in step with it.

If a controller is being relied upon to switch a kiln off, it is obviously essential that damage to the thermocouple should not prevent this operation. For this reason the manufacturers incorporate 'thermocouple break protection' or TCB. If the circuit is broken the black pointer is driven hard upscale to switch off the kiln supply. This will also, of course, cut the kiln firing before it reaches maturity, and may spoil the pots.

These expensive items of equipment may well save their cost in accident prevention where the potter or teacher cannot attend the kiln at all times.

NON-INDICATING CONTROLLERS

These are cheaper and will perform all the functions of the type discussed above but do not show the actual temperature reached in the kiln. This temperature can, however, be checked by rotating the knob on the front until the current switches off (shown by the 'set point' indicator lamp going out). The temperature in the kiln is seen by the setting on the dial. The knob must then be returned to the required switch-off temperature.

ENERGY REGULATORS

These are controls which automatically switch the kiln supply on and off at intervals which vary with the setting of the dial. The principle on which they work is that of a bimetal strip which bends upon being heated due to the different expansion of the two metals. Around the energy regulator is wound a coil of resistance wire which causes it to bend when energized with electric current. This is associated with a switch the contacts of which are normally closed. In this position current flows through the elements and also through the strip winding which heats it and causes it to deflect and open the switch contacts. The opening of the contacts interrupts the current flow, the heater winding is de-energized, and the strip is allowed to cool. In cooling it straightens, contacts are closed, and the cycle is repeated.

The calibrated knob on the control is connected to a cam which determines the degree of bending of the bimetal strip necessary to operate the contacts. At one extreme (0 on dial) the switch is open even when the strip is cold. At the other (100) contact is continuous. Graph 16 shows an average power/setting ratio. The controls are independent of the temperature in the kiln and simply regulate current on-off periods. They can, of course, be used in association with a controlling pyrometer.

The best known of the British regulators are the Simmerstat and the Sunvic (Satchwell Sunvic Ltd.). The Simmerstat can handle up to 13 amps direct but for larger loads the Sunvic models (ERY and ERX/L) operate through a contactor. The Robertshaw Infinite control (Diagram 76) is an American equivalent of the Simmerstat.

It is also possible to use variable transformers and thyristors but these are expensive and bulky. A cheaper variable system employing electronic circuits is being developed by Mike Harris (Dyrham, Wilts).

MULTIHEAT SWITCHING

Energy regulators operate on the whole load—on or off. It is also possible to cut the actual power generated through series-parallel switching. This requires at least two circuits of elements in the kiln. The low/medium/high settings of the switch operate as follows:

1. Low setting: two circuits in series, which reduce the power generated to one quarter.

EXAMPLE 2.
A kiln with 2 × 4000 watt circuits, totalling 8 kW at 240 V.

$$\text{Resistance} = \frac{E^2}{P} = \frac{240^2}{4000} = 14.4 \text{ ohms.}$$

Two circuits in series will exert 28.8 ohms.

$$\text{Power} = \frac{E^2}{R} = \frac{240^2}{28.8} = 2000 \text{ watts total power.}$$

2. Medium setting: power in one circuit only. Example 4kW.

3. High setting: both circuits at full power—8 kW.

Using two 120 V circuits with neutral as in the U.S. the positions are slightly different and give a very gentle low setting. There is often an off position in addition to the settings.

Diagrams 75, 76, and 77 show three simple wirings for the most common control systems.

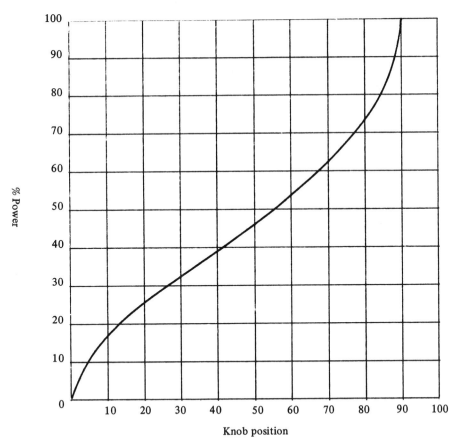

Graph 18. Typical energy regulator performance curve.

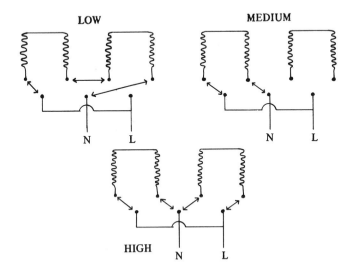

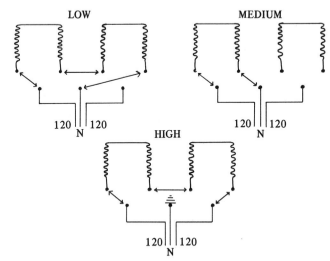

Diag. 73. Connections for a multi-position switch heat control.
Low: The current passes through two circuits in series which results in very little heat. For drying.
Medium: One circuit on only. For burning off wax etc.
High: Two circuits in parallel. Full power.

Diag. 74. Results from two 120 V circuits with neutral. (U.S.)
Low: very low heat—120 V through two circuits.
Medium: one circuit at 120 V.
High: two circuits at 240 V—full power. (Courtesy Wikey CCEK)

105

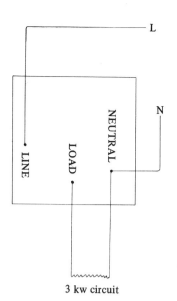

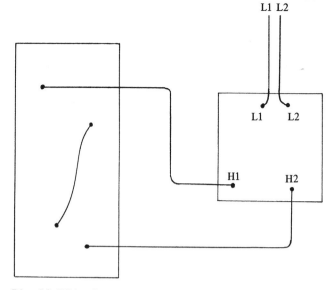

Diag. 75. A typical wiring diagram for a Simmerstat or similar small control. If circuits are kept to 3 kW maximum a control can be wired direct to each one independently. This is often done in small commercial kilns.

Diag. 76. Wiring for a Robertshaw Infinite Control (similar to Simmerstat). (Courtesy Paragon Industries, Inc.)

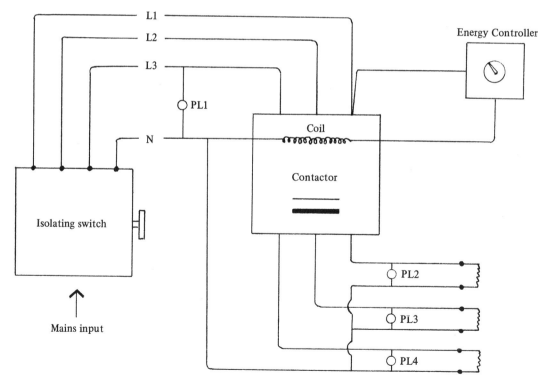

Diag. 77. Wiring diagram for Energy Regulator control though a Contactor. The coil in the Contactor is energized by the Regulator to make or break the circuits. The pilot light PL1 would remain on as long as the Isolator is switched on, irrespective of Controller.

PL2, 3 and 4 will light only when the contacts are in and current is flowing to the elements. They will indicate whether all circuits are in order. The diagram can represent a single phase supply to three circuits or a three-phase star system.

SHUT-OFF MECHANISMS USING CONES

There are mechanical systems on the market in which the bending of a pyrometeric cone operates a cut-off switch. These are often called 'kiln-sitters'. They are operated by a rod which pierces the kiln wall, one end of which rests on a cone (press-molded Junior type) set horizontally between two supports. The bending of the cone allows the end of the rod to fall, lifting a claw on the outside of the kiln and releasing a hinged weight which drops and strikes a plunger, switching the kiln off.

TIME SWITCH AND FAIL-SAFE FUSE

This is the final check in case the kiln-sitter, human or mechanical, fails to note that the firing is complete. A clock must, of course, be set at a guess of some twenty minutes or half an hour beyond the expected firing time. It can prevent gross overfiring and could be used in the cone touch-down procedure discussed on p. 100. The heat-fuse is used like a thermocouple and is connected to the supply through a contactor. It will melt at a given temperature which, as with the clock, must be in excess of the optimum firing temperature. It protects the shelving and the kiln itself rather than the wares.

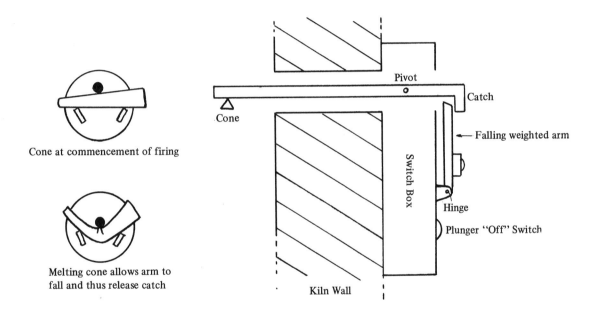

Cone at commencement of firing

Melting cone allows arm to fall and thus release catch

Diag. 78. A 'Kiln sitter' or automatic cone control.

9. Using Your Electric Kiln

DRYING

Pots, both of raw clay and glazed, should be thoroughly dry before packing. Drying in the kiln is not only liable to damage elements and connectors, but can be a frequent cause of glaze and body blisters. The kiln fabric is also very porous and may need drying out before packing if it has not been in regular use. See p. 103 for general advice on drying clay. Once pots are really dry (150/300°T) the biscuit firing can be quite fast up to 850/1560°T. A test for dryness is to place a piece of cold plastic sheet such as a plastic scraper, or a piece of cold glass or metal, momentarily over the mouth of a pot. Any steam will condense on the surface of the plastic and can be detected by passing one's finger across it.

PACKING

Placing in electric kilns is always open, i.e., no saggars are necessary. The evenness of the heat and the oxidizing conditions allow the use of comparatively thin shelves: $\frac{3}{8}$/9 mm to $\frac{1}{2}$/13 mm for spans up to 18/450 mm; $\frac{1}{2}$/13 mm or $\frac{5}{8}$/16 mm up to 24/600 mm for temperatures up to 1275/2320°T. The precaution of a support under the middle of the shelf may be taken with very heavy ware. The lighter batts leave more space available for pots and use less energy in firing. The kiln furniture may often have more bulk than the ware in the kiln. Space-saving is also achieved by the sensible placing of shelf supports: three for a single shelf; four for two side by side.

Diag. 79. Shelf supports. A. The wrong way to support a shelf batt. Not only is it likely to sag between the supports but it is also difficult to get the props level. B. Less props; more and steadier support. C. Four props for two shelves. D. The prop positions vary a little but the thrust is straight down through the pile. If props do not correspond, shelf warping is more likely, Heavy pieces should not be placed on a variable prop system.

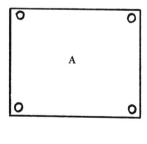

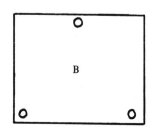

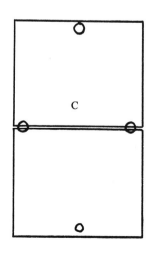

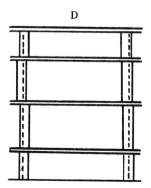

Although there is little convection in a closed kiln, staggering shelves will assist the even distribution of heat.

When packing top-loaders, the plan of the load is always evident and the pots can be fitted very close together without danger. The height, however, must be checked before a shelf is laid on the props: this is done by laying a suitable length of 1/25 by $\frac{1}{2}$/12 mm timber across the props. Two or three pieces of wood of different lengths will be needed. A spirit level is an added check.

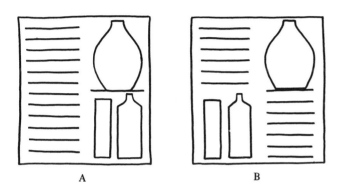

Diag. 80. Shelf and pack distribution. **A** is likely to cause uneven heating and firing; **B** is a better distribution.

Ill. 50. The use of a batten for testing the height of pots to ensure that the shelf will not touch down on them.

Shelf and ware density will affect firing, but there is sometimes confusion as to its effect. Certainly a tighter pack will take longer to fire. In the matter of local effect, however, if, for instance, the bottom of a kiln is too hot, a potter's first reaction might be to raise the floor batts or to pack more loosely to "let the heat get away." This might work in a fuelled, hot-gas heated kiln, but with radiant heat the opposite is true—it is more effective to pack the floor closely with shelves and pots so that the heat produced has more work to do. A *cool* floor needs more open packing. For the same reason it is not advisable to stack one large area with tiles or other flatware. If you wish to fire a lot of tiles, very thin individual setters should be used. They can be bought with built-in spacing pieces.

Although silicon carbide is a conductor of electricity, the shelves are clay-bonded and this renders them safe to use in an electric kiln. They are expensive but are splendid conductors of heat and are especially useful as floor batts. Glaze chips very easily from this material.

In time shelves will develop a warp or curve. They can then be turned upside down and will tend to flatten again. For this reason I recommend a thin sprinkling of coarse alumina (or crushed waste from cutting H.T. insulating bricks) at each firing rather than the more permanent batt-washes which are available. Porcelain is best set on individual discs which have been lightly washed over with a 1/1 mixture of calcined alumina and china clay made up as a thin slip.

FIRING

The clay bodies you use and your particular methods of working will determine your firing schedules but, with the increasing worldwide shortage of energy and its high cost, a rapid and economic fire is obviously desirable where possible. Very slow firing will bring the kiln fabric near to maximum heat capacity *and* maximum radiation. The excessive heating of the kiln itself is a waste of energy. Leaving a kiln at 'low' overnight, for instance, is extravagant use of current. If you can still put your hand on the outer skin of the kiln when the chamber is at 1250/2280°T, then both kiln and firing are likely to be economic.

The watt-loadings suggested in this book tend towards high-maximum power and the consequent possibility of shorter firings. Sophisticated controls on the rate of heat rise will also demand a kiln which is capable of a fast climb to top temperature. With a variety of clay bodies, many of them free of any grog or sand, and including porcelain, I personally rarely spend more than five-and-one-half hours (often nearer four) on a biscuit fire to 975/1785°T, or nine hours on 1275/2325°T stoneware. For earthenware glazes up to 1125/2055°T there is less time for heat transference through the pack, and a twenty minute 'soak' or a slower rise near top temperature is almost always an asset.

Most electric kilns are indoors, often in the studio, and, since there is no chimney, ventilation will become a problem with certain types of clay or glaze. Site the kiln where possible near a window that can be opened. As mentioned in the Introduction, the provision of a 'chimney' or vent direct from kiln through the wall will be likely to prevent your kiln from ever reaching top temperature. The sulfurous smells from some clays or the smoke from burning wax are not good to breath and it is as well to vacate the kiln room when they are at their worst. Lead glazes can volatilize and the chamber should be allowed to become near cold before unpacking.

BISCUIT FIRE

Fully dry pots can be heated up to 850/1560°T quite quickly: four to eight hours according to size and thickness. The change from clay into pot at around 600/1110°T is considered by some scientists to be almost instantaneous and the experience of primitive potters who burn very large pieces in a bonfire to a fairly firm fabric in twenty minutes or so tends to confirm this. Bone-china biscuit has been experimentally vitrified in seven minutes. For clays which contain a lot of carbon a slightly slower rise from 800/1470°T to 1000/1830°T is reputed to help avoid bloating in the subsequent glaze fire. It is my experience that this 'disease' is often the result of taking the body above its optimum temperature in the glaze firing; a reduction of even 10/18 degrees will often cure the problem. At 450/840°T to 650/1200°T combined water will be released and steam will be seen escaping from the kiln. Loosen the bung or ventilator over this period to prevent the vapor being forced out through the element tail holes thereby corroding the element-tail connections.

GLAZE FIRE

The schedule will vary with every potter, but little change occurs in glazes below about 700/1290°T for earthenwares and 1000/1830°T for stonewares. The significant period starts about 150/280 degrees below the maturing temperature. A fast firing over the first two-thirds of the range is therefore recommended so long as the pots are quite dry before firing starts. The burning off of wax resist will take an hour or more at about 150/300°T. All smoking should have ceased before the kiln is finally closed. Toploaders should not be bricked over during this operation:

one roof bat can be propped on a piece of ceramic. The lid will get very hot and you will need a suitable metal tool such as a turning tool to lower it into place.

The heat from the elements is radiant: large flat surfaces should not be set close to a bank of elements. It will also be noticed that flat pieces, such as plates, fire to a different color and surface texture compared with the same glaze on an upright surface. This is an inherent weakness of radiant heat which will strike only the edge of a plate while heating the whole of a vertical surface. It is advisable to glaze plates a little thinner and/or to place them in a part of the chamber known to be warmer, possibly near the floor, from which heat radiates upward. Do not stack more than three or four layers of flatware together.

REDUCTION

The normal atmosphere in electric kilns is neutral or slightly oxidizing, and it is better to fully exploit this situation rather than attempt the more contrived business of setting up a reducing atmosphere. However, there are a number of methods and the following suggestions have been derived mainly from conversations with Peter Smith, a potter and ceramic chemist, and his articles in *Ceramic Review*.

Reduction behavior is summarized by the conversion of carbon monoxide to carbon dioxide and to a lesser degree hydrogen to water vapor. Carbon itself will also give a reduction reaction when used as an addition to the glaze. Only in exceptional circumstances do molten glazes contain distinct compounds such as those from which they were originally mixed. For instance, a 'celadon' glaze will consist of cations (Fe^{2+}) and anions (O^{2-}) surrounded by a loose structure of all the other species in the glaze. The gases CO and H_2 affect the state of oxidation of the reducible metals in the glaze, for instance ferrous (Fe^{2+}) and ferric (Fe^{3+}) ions are produced in the celadon glaze and the proportions of each in the glaze matrix determines the color. Iron is rarely reduced to the metal but copper oxide is more easily reducible from cupric to cuprous and right through to the metal. The more pot and glaze surface the gas can reach, the greater the chances of reduction being achieved; it is essential for the gases to wash over the surface. Once reduction is effective the smooth surface of the glaze inhibits re-oxidation during cooling except where the glaze is thinner on throwing rings and edges, thus giving the iron red highlights on tenmoku-type high-iron glazes.

If the whole of an electric kiln chamber is to be reduced by means of gases, a high rate of gas production must be maintained. This means that the kiln has to be adapted and a liberal number of feed-pipes introduced. All cracks should be sealed with grogged clay, ceramic fiber, etc. Substances available for consuming the oxygen and providing a reducing atmosphere are any burnable or organic material: wood, coal, coke, charcoal, wax, oils, camphor (mothballs), soap, sugar, and gases to mention the most common. Devices such as push rods can be used to help solids into the kiln. The rate of feed is best judged by keeping a small but steady flow of smoke leaking out. Reduction can start at about 1100/2010°T and continue to the end of the firing. Smoke and/or carbon monoxide are a necessary product: good ventilation is therefore essential. Mothballs can be dropped down tubes into the kiln at the rate of about 500 gms/hr. This is a very effective substance as is wax in the form of pieces of candle wrapped in wet paper. Liquids are more dangerous because of their low flash points and oil should be used as a flame from a burner. Small supply gas or propane burners can also be used and are easier to handle and control. Fred Olsen in *The Kiln Book* shows an electric kiln built with firemouth and chimney. I have doubts about this design reaching temperatures where iron reduction can take place.

It must be remembered that reducing agents attack wire elements. Reduction by carbon and gases in the atmosphere of an electric kiln can give at best a quiet, subtle glaze. Results will be variable according to the proximity of pots to the points of addition of reducing agents.

A much more convenient and perhaps more effective system is to introduce carbon or carbides into the glaze itself: the reduction reaction is then Fe_2O_3 into $3Fe + 2CO$. In practice the reduction is to ferrous iron rather than the metal. The necessary carbon is often introduced willy-nilly into the glaze when ash is used as an ingredient. Other sources include coal dust, coke, graphite, coal ash, and charcoals. To use the more purely carbon materials, all that is necessary is to add about 10 percent by weight to the glaze recipe. A finer sieve (100 or 120 mesh) will help distribute the carbon particles, but different treatments can be tried. Pots are glazed in the normal manner. This method gives so little carbon monoxide in the kiln that the elements are not significantly affected. Silicon carbide (300 mesh) can be used in additions of 2 to 5 percent. More can cause craters in the glaze—it continues reacting as the glaze cools. Chemicals suitable for reduction can be obtained from B D H Chemicals Ltd., Poole, Dorset BH12 4NN, England and Hopkin & Williams, Freshwater Road, Chadwell Heath, Essex, P.B.O. 1, Romford RM1 1HA, England.

In metal-based elements such as Kanthal, the alumina content has great affinity for oxygen and quickly forms a protective alumina layer. This layer is adversely affected by many reducing agents. Only cracked ammonia and pure hydrogen are listed as nonharmful in the Kanthal Handbook, and even these only to certain temperatures, as the following table shows.

A1 wire	can be taken to
In dry air	1375/2505°T
In moist air	1300/2370°T
In hydrogen	1375/2505°T
In cracked ammonia	1200/2190°T
In carbon dioxide	1100/1920°T
In town gas	1050/1920°T

This does not mean that the elements will immediately fail if the warnings are disregarded, but they will undoubtedly be attacked to some degree. Potters have, in fact, reduced in wired kilns for long periods without failure.

According to the information issued by the makers of silicon-carbide rods these, also, can suffer from certain reducing conditions which also impose a low watt-loss figure. The glazed type of rod is less susceptible to attack than the plain silicon carbide. Compared with wire, however, reduction is a much more practical proposition, and can be operated at higher temperatures. See Chapter 6.

RAKU

Raku firing involves both filling and emptying the kiln at the glaze maturing temperature. Long metal tongs are used. *Any attempt to perform this difficult operation while any element or connection of an electric kiln is exposed could be (literally) fatal*, and at the very least lead to burns and injury.

A complete inner muffle must therefore be provided and many designs have been worked out to this end. It is advisable, for reasons of heat loss and convenience, to use a small kiln for the purpose—around a 14-inch cube is excellent—either front- or top-loading. If it is small enough to be transportable, this is a valuable bonus: it can then be moved to a site near an outside door for reduction techniques which can then take place in the open air. If regular raku firings are envisaged, a fairly cheap purpose-built kiln can be constructed. It can double up for low-biscuit or enamel firings.

The muffle may be slab or coil built with the turned out rim fitting into the rebates at the top of the wall as snugly as possible. Allow for about 10-percent shrinkage. A well-grogged clay must be used. A loose floor or kiln shelf cut to fit will extend its life and can be renewed. A silicon-carbide bat would be ideal but expensive.

Specifications for a small top-loader raku kiln, as seen in Illustrations 51 and 52, will be found in Chapter 10 (kiln 5). The inner muffle *must* be used as illustrated. Without a muffle the kiln is suitable for ordinary firings up to about 1050/1920°T.

For front-loaders (without elements in the door) a similar type of muffle as illustrated in Diagram 81 may be made and supported on bat supports. The space between the muf-fle face and the wall of a larger kiln should be filled with insulating bricks as in Diagram 82.

Michael Crossley-Jones in the first issue of *Ceramic Review*, suggests a muffle of thin bats set in slots in quarter bricks which rest on a kiln shelf. The front, again, is blocked round with insulating bricks. The system seems to me to be a little unstable for the rather hectic conditions of raku loading and drawing. The upright walls could be taken to

Ill. 51. A special muffle or saggar for a top-loading kiln to enable it to be used without danger for raku. The wide rim or flange round the top holds the saggar walls about 1.5/35 mm from the kiln elements.

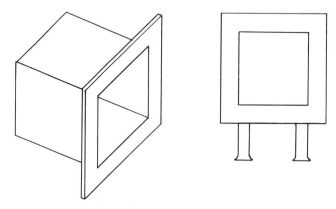

Diag. 81. Muffle and supports.

Ill. 52. The saggar in position, showing the lid with a hole in the center for lifting. One's finger would not be used with the kiln firing! An iron hook or tongs would be needed.

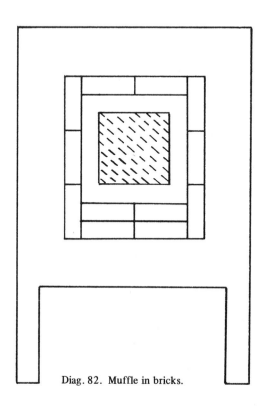

Diag. 82. Muffle in bricks.

the roof if this were arched to prevent their falling out-wards. I would also replace the quarter bricks with whole ones, cut with a groove near one face (see Diagram 83).

As previously mentioned a loose, renewable floor is an asset.

FIRING

Bring the closed muffle up to temperature using either a cone or a pyrometer, or visual judgement. A trial glazed piece can also be used. With a small kiln, opening up for packing and drawing will depress the temperature a little and time must be allowed for it to recover—with the kiln in Illustrations 51 and 52, only twenty minutes or so. Where a more powerful kiln is used it may be necessary to switch on and off or to use a Sunvic or similar regulator.

A pyrometer is a useful adjunct to a raku kiln adaptation but the thermocouple must penetrate into the actual muf-fle. A hole can be cut in the muffle to line up with that in the kiln wall. This should be twice the size of the thermo-couple to allow for any movement. If the bat-built muffle is used it can extend to the back wall of the kiln (which must not contain elements) where the thermocouple is often situated. Alternatively a cone can be put in the muffle when cold and extracted as soon as it squats, when firing can commence. After this the state of the glazes will indicate the temperature.

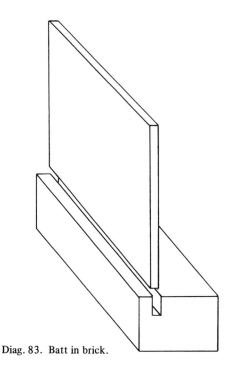

Diag. 83. Batt in brick.

SITING

A good deal of very hot air is going to escape when the muffle is opened. Leave plenty of room around the kiln, and site it preferably on a fire-proof floor. The ceiling should not be too low and should not be lined with easily inflammable material (polystyrene tiles are often very dan-gerous in this respect). On a really fine day the kiln could be sited outside (with a suitably protected lead) but must be disconnected at the slightest sign of rain or very damp atmosphere.

A NOTE ABOUT COMMERCIAL KILNS

The industrially built kiln will often be more robust in construction than that made by the average potter. It will be compact in its controls and, in England at any rate, usu-ally equipped with door switches and other refinements which make it virtually foolproof against electric shock. This is necessary when the kiln is to be used in a school by a number of pupils and teachers. It may not, however, be a better instrument for firing than one the potter can make himself. It will be difficult to alter the heat distribution in a commercially-made kiln if this is found desirable. Many are still built with all-brick walls and are consequently very heavy and consume a good deal of energy in heating them at each firing. In America the opposite characteristics seem to prevail: very light, thin-walled kilns with rapid heating and cooling cycles are common. As seen in Graph 5, p. 43, their power/volume ratio is lower than those made in the U.K. (or those recommended in this book) and it is difficult to believe all the details of performance as given in manu-facturers' brochures. One company quotes 1350/2460°T attainable in a wire-element kiln: this is 40/70 degrees be-yond any claim made by the wire manufacturers.

When considering buying a kiln, decide just what you want and what you want it to do. Then approach the manu-facturers and specify your requirements. The onus for its eventual performance will then lie with them—especially if you can induce the manufacturer to produce a letter pro-mising results. You can rightly complain if it does not match up to the specification. (But complain to the manufacturer, not to me!) You are more than likely to be satisfied with a commercial kiln but I would always recommend the above procedure—just in case.

TABLE 13

Extract from the I.E.E. Regulations, 14th Edition. Tables 1M and 3M.

Copper conductor nominal C.S.A. mm^2	Single core cables, run in conduit or duct.	
	single-phase (2 cables) rating (amperes)	3-phase (3 cables) rating (amperes)
1.0	11	9.0
1.5	13	11
2.5	18	16
4.0	24	22
6.0	31	28
10.0	42	39
16.0	56	50
25.0	73	66
35.0	90	80
50.0	145	125

Copper conductor nominal C.S.A. mm^2	Twin or multicore cables, sheathed, clipped direct to a surface (unenclosed)	
	One twin with earth continuity conductor rating (amperes)	One 3 or 4 core with earth continuity conductor rating (amperes)
1.0	11	9.0
1.5	13	12
2.5	18	16
4.0	24	22
6.0	30	27
10.0	40	37
16.00	53	47
25.0	60	53
35.0	74	65
50.0	140	125

C.S.A. = cross sectional area

TABLE 14
Characteristics of Kanthal Al Wire

Gauge	No.	Diam. in.	Diam. mm.	Ohms/ft 20/68°T	Ohms/m 20/68°T	in²/ft	cm²/m	ft/lb	m/kg	in²/Ω 20/68°T	cm²/Ω 20/68°T
AWG	8	.129	3.26	.053		4.84		25		91.7	
SWG	10	.128	3.25	.053		4.83		25.2		90.6	
			3.25		.175		102.1		17		584.2
			3.00		.205		94.2		19.9		459.5
SWG	11	.116	2.95	.065		4.37		30.7		67.5	
AWG	9	.114	2.91	.067		4.31		31.6		64.7	
			2.8		.235		88.		22.9		373.5
SWG	12	.104	2.64	.081		3.92		38.2		48.6	
			2.6		.273		81.7		26.5		299.2
AWG	10	.102	2.59	.084		3.84		39.9		45.7	
			2.50		.295		78.5		28.4		266
			2.4		.320		75.4		31.1		235.2
SWG	13	.092	2.34	.103		3.47		48.9		36.7	
AWG	11	.091	2.3	.106		3.42		50.3		32.3	
			2.3		.349		72.3		33.9		207.1
			2.2		.381		69.2		37.		181.2
AWG	12	.081	2.05	.133		3.05		63.4		22.8	
SWG	14	.08	2.03	.136		3.02		64.6		22.1	
			2.0		.462		62.8		44.8		136.1
			1.9		.511		59.7		49.7		117.3
SWG	15	.072	1.83	.168		2.71		78.8		16.1	
AWG	13	.072	1.83	.168		2.71		79		16.1	
			1.8		.57		56.5		55.3		99.2
			1.7		.64		53.4		62		83.6
AWG	14	.064	1.63	.212		2.42		101.0		11.4	
SWG	16	.064	1.63	.213		2.41		101.0		11.3	
			1.6		.721		50.3		70.0		69.7
			1.5		.82		47.1		79.7		57.4
AWG	15	.057	1.45	.268		2.15		127.1		8.0	
SWG	17	.056	1.42	.278		2.11		131.9		7.6	
			1.4		.942		44.0		91.5		46.7
			1.3		1.092		40.8		106.1		37.3
AWG	16	.051	1.29	.338		1.92		160.3		5.7	
SWG	18	.048	1.22	.379		1.81		179.4		4.8	
			1.2		1.282		37.7		124.5		29.4

TABLE 15
Ct Factors for Kanthal A1 Wire

Ct factor. Increase of resistance with temperature. °T

700/	800/	900/	1000/	1100/	1200/	1300/	1350/
1290	1470	1650	1830	2010	2190	2370	2460
1.023	1.028	1.032	1.036	1.038	1.040	1.042	1.043

See also Graph 9.

TABLE 17
Cone Equivalent Table

This *Cone Equivalent Table* is an indication of probable squatting temperatures, always to be checked against results in your own kiln.

No	Seger	Staffs	Orton
022	600/1112	600/1112	600/1112
018	710/1310	710/1310	717/1323
017	730/1347	730/1347	747/1377
016	750/1382	750/1382	792/1457
015		790/1454	804/1479
015a	790/1454		
014			
014a	815/1498	815/1498	838/1541
012			
012a	855/1571	855/1571	884/1623
010		900/1652	894/1641
010a	900/1652		
09		920/1688	923/1693
09a	920/1688		
08		940/1724	955/1750
08a	940/1724		
07		960/1760	984/1803
07a	960/1760	970/1755	
06		980/1796	999/1830
06a	980/1796	990/1813	
05		1000/1832	1046/1915
05a	1000/1832	1010/1850	
04		1020/1868	1060/1940
04a	1020/1868	1030/1884	
03		1040/1903	1101/2014
03a	1040/1903	1050/1922	
02		1060/1940	1120/2048
02a	1060/1940	1070/1958	
01		1080/1976	1137/2049
01a	1080/1976	1090/1994	

No	Seger	Staffs	Orton
1		1100/2012	1154/2109
1a	1100/2012	1110/2030	
2		1120/2048	1162/2143
2a	1120/2048	1130/2066	
3		1140/2054	1168/2135
3a	1140/2054	1150/2102	
4		1160/2120	1186/2168
4a	1160/2120	1170/2138	
5		1180/2156	1196/2185
5a	1180/2156	1190/2174	
6		1200/2192	1222/2231
6a	1200/2192	1215/2218	
7	1230/2246	1230/2246	1240/2264
7a		1240/2264	
8	1250/2282	1250/2282	1263/2305
8a		1260/2300	
9	1280/2336	1280/2336	1280/2336
9a		1290/2354	
10	1300/2372	1300/2372	1305/2381
10a		1310/2390	
11	1320/2408	1320/2408	1315/2400
12	1350/2462	1350/2462	1326/2418
13	1380/2516	1380/2516	1346/2455
14	1410/2570	1410/2570	1366/2495
15	1436/2617	1436/2617	1431/2608

TABLE 16
Physical and Thermal Properties of Molers Insulating Bricks and Mortars

| Bricks | Classification Temperature | Cold Crushing Strength lb/in² | Permanent Linear Change after 24 hrs at 30/50°T below Classification % | Reversible Thermal Expansion 20–1000°C % | True Porosity % | Thermal Conductivity Btu in/ft² hr °F at Mean Temperature °T | | | | | | Chemical Analysis | | | |
						205/400	425/800	650/1200	870/1600	1095/2000	1315/2400	Al_2O_3	Fe_2O_3	TiO_2	Alkalis
Moler Porous (34)	870/1600	200	0.5	0.17 ⎫	76	0.82	1.05	1.31				10.2	5.6	0.6	1.7
Moler Solid (45)	870/1600	700	0.7	0.17 ⎬ 800/1470°T	69	0.93	1.12	1.31				10.2	5.6	0.6	1.7
Moler Rotel (48)	920/1690	1420	1.0	0.17 ⎭	67	1.26	1.31	1.45				10.9	4.0	0.6	1.7
MPK 18/25	980/1800	180	0.1	0.7	85	0.94	1.13	1.35	1.6			24.1	4.0	1.3	2.7
MPK 20/26	1100/2000	220	0.5	0.7	84	1.08	1.26	1.48	1.77			24.1	4.0	1.3	2.7
MPK 20/36	1100/2000	420	0.5	0.6	78	1.42	1.66	1.89	2.12			26.9	3.2	1.3	2.5
MPK 23/42	1260/2300	350	0.3	0.4	75	1.13	1.29	1.45	1.61	1.77		36.0	1.0	−	2.2
MPK 23/48	1260/2300	500	0.5	0.5	71	1.59	1.8	2.08	2.41	2.77		35.2	1.5	0.9	3.0
MPK 23/60	1260/2300	800	0.5	0.5	64	2.04	2.23	2.48	2.81	3.2		36.6	1.4	0.7	2.7
MPK 25/44	1370/2500	300	0.4	0.5	75	1.44	1.55	1.71	1.94	2.24		40.2	0.4	0.6	0.9
MPK 25/54	1370/2500	700	0.4	0.5	67	1.87	2.08	2.29	2.50	2.71		42.2	1.3	0.3	2.0
MPK 26/48	1425/2600	400	0.4	0.5	73	2.02	2.18	2.36	2.56	2.79		47.0	0.5	1.6	1.1
MPK 26/57	1425/2600	900	0.5	0.5	64	1.98	2.16	2.36	2.56	2.8		42.2	1.3	0.3	2.0
MPK 28/55	1540/2800	550	0.3	0.5	72	2.29	2.38	2.48	2.59	2.72	2.89	61.0	0.3	0.7	0.7

| Mortars | Range | Setting Mechanism | Usage per 1000 76 mm Squares (114 mm Brickwork) Kg | Recommended Joint Thickness mm | Standard Packing | Chemical Analysis | | | | |
						Al_2O_3	Fe_2O_3	TiO_2	Alkalis	
Dribrick	Moler Solid, Porous, Rotol	Hydraulic/ Heat set	150	3	25 Kg bags	7.9	4.5	0.5	1.2	Powder. Mix with clean water.
MPK Rockbond	MPK 18/25 to 23/80 incl.	Partial Airset/ Heat set	200	1.5	25 Kg bags	28.7	3.9	1.4	2.3	Powder. Mix with clean water.
MPK Mortar	MPK 18/25 to 28/55 incl.	Heat set	200	1.5	25 Kg bags	41.6	1.4	0.3	2.1	Powder. Mix with clean water.
MPK Liquid Mortar	MPK 18/25 to 28/55 incl.	Full Airset/ Heat set	150	1.5	25 Kg pails UK 50 Kg drums	38.8	0.7	0.1	3.8	Ready to use. May be further let down with clean water.
MPK AS	MPK 18/25 to 28/55 incl.	Full Airset/ Heat set	125	1.5	25 Kg bags	38.9	0.7	0.1	3.8	Powder. Alternative to liquid.
MPK 30	MPK 30/67	Full Airset/ Heat set	150	1.5	25 Kg pails UK 50 Kg drums	70.0	0.4	0.1	2.5	Ready to use mortar.

TABLE 18
**Temperature Conversion Table—Centigrade (Celsius)
Fahrenheit**

C	F	C	F	C	F
0	32	816	1500	1210	2210
10	50	830	1526	1220	2228
24	75	840	1544	1230	2246
50	122	844	1550	1233	2250
66	150	850	1562	1240	2264
75	167	860	1580	1250	2282
93	200	870	1598	1260	2300
100	212	871	1600	1270	2318
121	250	880	1616	1280	2336
150	302	900	1652	1290	2354
177	350	920	1688	1300	2372
200	392	927	1700	1310	2390
204	400	940	1724	1315	2400
232	450	955	1750	1320	2408
250	482	960	1760	1330	2426
260	500	980	1796	1340	2444
300	572	982	1800	1343	2450
316	600	1000	1832	1350	2462
350	662	1010	1850	1360	2480
371	700	1020	1868	1371	2500
400	752	1038	1900	1380	2516
426	800	1050	1922	1390	2534
450	842	1060	1940	1400	2552
482	900	1070	1958	1450	2640
500	932	1080	1976	1500	2732
510	950	1090	1994		
550	1022	1094	2000		
566	1050	1100	2012		
573	1063	1110	2030		
593	1100	1121	2050		
600	1112	1130	2066		
621	1150	1140	2054		
650	1202	1150	2102		
677	1250	1160	2120		
700	1292	1165	2129		
704	1300	1170	2138		
725	1338	1177	2150		
732	1350	1180	2156		
750	1382	1190	2174		
760	1400	1200	2192		
800	1472	1206	2200		

10. Calculation of Materials and Specifications for Five Kilns

To convert Centigrade into Fahrenheit: divide by 5; multiply by 9; add 32.
To convert Fahrenheit into Centigrade: subtract 32; divide by 9; multiply by 5.

One can work out the requirements for a kiln by drawing it to scale, counting the bricks needed, measuring the angle and sheet material, etc. It is also possible to work out quantities by arithmetic.

Four factors will control the amount of material required:
1. The size of the chamber.
2. The thickness of the hot-face walls.
3. The thickness of the insulating walls.
4. The type of kiln—top- or front-loader—which mainly affects the length of metal angle and arch bricks if these are used.

It will be necessary to give these factors symbols:
1. Chamber: A (long wall length) $\times$ B (short wall) $\times$ C (height).
2. Hot-face walls: H units thick.
3. Insulation: I units thick.
4. Top-loader: TL. Front-loader: FL.
5. Two additional symbols will indicate the surface area or face of the brick, insulator etc. If standard bricks are laid flat the wall thickness will be $4\frac{1}{2}$ inches and the face of the brick in the kiln will be 9×3 inches ($9 \times 2\frac{1}{2}$ in the U.S.); if on edge the face will be $9 \times 4\frac{1}{2}$ inches. Areas 27 in^2 and 40.5 in^2 respectively. Thus brick face area is shown by Bf, insulator slab area (often 36×12 in) Sf, Asbestolux Af (usually 96×48 in).

The unit of length to remain constant throughout, i.e., inches, centimeters, or millimeters.

HOT-FACE MATERIAL

Floor: $\dfrac{(A + 2H) \times (B + 2H)}{Bf}$ = number of bricks.

Roof: TL and flat roofed FL similar to above. Arch bricks will be $\dfrac{A \times B}{Bf}$ plus skews and side bricks.

Walls: $2 \times \dfrac{(A + 2H) \times C}{Bf} + 2 \times \dfrac{B \times C}{Bf}$

INSULATING MATERIAL

Floor: $\dfrac{(A + 2H + 2I) \times (B + 2H + 2I)}{If}$ = number of slabs of insulator.

Roof: same as floor.

Walls: $2 \times \dfrac{(A + 2H + 2I) \times (C + H)}{If}$

$+ 2 \times \dfrac{(B + 2H) \times (C + H)}{If}$

CLADDING (ASBESTOLUX, SHEET METAL)

Floor: $\dfrac{\text{as insulating material area}}{Af}$
&
Roof:

Walls: $2 \times \dfrac{(A + 2H + 2I) \times (C + H + I)}{Af}$

$+ 2 \times \dfrac{(B + 2H + 2I) \times (C + H + I)}{Af}$

WIRE

Weight for total for all circuits can be found by dividing the length required by the length per pound or kilo as shown in Table 14. Example: 400 feet of 14 swg at 64.6 feet/lb = $\dfrac{400}{64.6}$ = 6.2 lbs.

METAL ANGLE

This will vary with the design but for a TL built as suggested in this book the total length would be in the region of:

$(A + 2H + 2I + 6/160 \text{ mm}) \times 5$
$(B + 2H + 2I) \times 8$
$(C + H + I) \times 4$

Extra angle will be needed for casing in top insulator if this is done.

CONNECTORS

Twice as many as elements.

ASBESTOS-COVERED WIRE

$1\frac{1}{2}$ to 2 yards for connections plus distance from kiln to isolating switch multiplied by two for single-phase, and by four for three-phase.

SAMPLE SPECIFICATIONS FOR 5 KILNS

The following specifications are intended as examples of some of the principles of electric kiln building as described in this book. Every potter will have his own requirements so that kiln plans as such will never satisfy more than a few. Any significant alteration in the use or size of a kiln will often lead to a redesigning of the whole kiln.

The two top-loaders are similar to models I have built and used for years with satisfactory results. The lower-temperature front-loader is based on my experience but has not been built in precisely this form. It illustrates the power-to-volume ratio and the thinner insulation suitable for firing below 1150/2100°T. These kilns are designed to reach top temperature in eight to ten hours. The SiC-rod kiln is reproduced by kind permission of Peter Taylor (Labheat).

KILN 1. SMALL TOP-LOADER TO FIRE TO 1280/2335°T
Muffle size: 12/305 mm × 18/457 mm × 11/280 mm high
Exterior: 24.5/625 × 35.5/900 mm × 25/330 mm high
Top-loader: one circuit, 5 kW, 240 V

MATERIALS

Lengths of Dexion metal angle or similar material	5	35.5/900 mm length
	4	25/330 mm
	8	23.75/604 mm
Sheets of $\frac{1}{4}$/6 mm Asbestolux or similar material (Transite)	2	17/432 mm × 35/895 mm
	4	17/432 mm × 23/585 mm
	2	23.5/587 mm × 30/762 mm
	2	24/610 mm × 3/76 mm
White H.T. K25 Insulating bricks	82	9/228 × 4.5/174 mm × 3/76 mm
	(100 if only 2.5/63 mm thick)	
Caposil or similar high-insulation blocks	2	12/305 mm × 30/762 mm × 1.5/38 mm
	2	12/305 mm × 30/762 mm × 1/25 mm
	2	12/305 mm × 21/533 mm × 1.5/38 mm
Either Caposil or 4.5/115 mm insulating bricks or slabs for 900/1650°T		To cover area 27/685 mm × 23/585 mm
Kanthal A1 13 swg resistance wire	130/40 m	(order 4 lbs to allow for spares)
Electrical sundries	22	line taps
	2.5 yards (2 m)	4 mm asbestos covered wire
	1	30 ampere fuse box and isolating switch wire, etc. for installation
Roof tiles (Alumina)	2	13.5/342 mm × 9.75/248 mm × 0.625/16 mm
Shelves (Suggested)	3	17/432 mm × 11/280 × .5/12 mm
	3	11/280 mm × 8.5/215 × .375/9 mm props, etc.

METHOD

1. Cut the two larger sheets of Asbestolux (17 × 35), two 17 × 23, and the 23.5 × 30 floor sheet. N.B. *Use dust mask* when cutting asbestos and when sweeping or moving dust.

2. Cut and assemble metal frame, placing asbestos sheets in position before bolting up; see Diagram 84. N.B. It will be necessary to cut or drill slots in sheeting where fitting is impeded by bolts.

3. Cut Caposil to size for floor and lay on asbestos sheet (1 inch).

4. Cut and lay $4\frac{1}{2}$-inch layer of H.T. insulating bricks on Caposil.

5. Cut and insert $1\frac{1}{2}$-inch sheets of Caposil as outer insulating skin.

6. Cut and fit $4\frac{1}{2}$-inch thick walls of H.T. insulating brick. You should now be left with a 12 × 18 × 12 chamber.

7. Check that the top surfaces of brick and Caposil are level.

8. With a ruler and colored pencil or crayon mark the roof shelf recess and the element slots in walls and floor. Number or other wise indicate position of the bricks.

9. Remove H.T. bricks which are marked and cut grooves and recesses. Also, cut narrow upright grooves for straight sections of hairpin elements.

10. Reassemble bricks. A hoop of element wire may be inserted as shown in Diagram 30, p. 50 (at each level) to keep bricks from moving inwards.

11. Drill holes for element tails. A simple $\frac{1}{4}$- or $\frac{3}{8}$-inch metal rod about 12 inches long and filed to a pointed wedge at the end will cut through bricks and sheeting. Use an electric drill and work from inside the muffle. The holes can be angled for convenience in drilling. See p. 59, Illustration 25 and Diagram 52.

12. Twist element tails and wind element coils on a $\frac{3}{8}$-inch mandrel.

13. Stretch elements to fit slots. Grip one end in a vice and pull steadily from the other end to attain even spacing of coils. N.B. Do not grip wire with metal tools if possible. A nick or serious abrasion may lead to burn-out.

14. Insert elements.

15. Connect up tails as in Diagram 55 on p. 79 with asbestos-covered wire, and connect to switchbox.

16. Take earth wire or wires from frame and connect.

17. Bolt strips 24 × 3 of Asbestolux onto tops of connector boxes and sheets $17\frac{1}{2}$ × 23 onto either end.

18. Roof: The two alumina bats (shelves), $13\frac{1}{2}$ × $9\frac{3}{4}$ × $\frac{5}{8}$ drop into the recess round the top of the firing chamber. Finger slots for lowering and lifting them should be cut for one shelf only. A 3-inch layer of H.T. bricks is laid over the whole area of the top of the kiln inside the angle iron frame—3 bricks along the 30-inch side by 5 bricks along the shorter side. These cover 27 × $22\frac{1}{2}$ inches. On the bricks are laid the sheets of 2-inch Caposil (or $23\frac{1}{2}$ × 30 sheet of Asbestolux).

Caposil is dusty and liable to chip. If used for the roof it would help if it were set in an angle-iron frame with the Asbestolux bolted through to the angle, sandwiching the Caposil between. In this case the block should be made large enough for the angle to hang beyond the layer of H.T. bricks so that the Caposil surface is in direct contact with them. Alternatively the outer ring of bricks could be recessed slightly to take the metal. See pp. 52–53, Diagrams 33 and 34 and Illustration 19.

19. Elements: Wire lengths to be cut 3 each of 17.5/5.34 m, 6 each of 9.75/2.97 m, and 1 of 23/7 m. These lengths allow for 9/225 mm on each end to be turned back and twisted together. The first three elements and four of the 9.75 feet are wound as hairpins; the rest are wound as one length. They form a single circuit.

20. Slot positions on all walls (centers measured from floor): 1.75/45 mm, 5.75/145 mm, 9/228 mm, 10.75/273 mm.

21. Floor batt, 0.5/12 mm, should just clear the elements. Take care that short-wall elements terminate at least 0.5/12 mm from the corners to avoid possible contact with the long-wall elements. Tail holes are sloped apart as in Diagram 52.

This kiln which was designed for a Potters Camp demonstration was built complete with fitted elements and was ready to fire in ten hours. It has now been in use for firing porcelain and is quite efficient. It attains 1270/2315°T in eight hours from cold.

The plan of bricks, etc., in this kiln will be found on p. 50 and p. 59 illustrating Kanthal wire brick hoops and tail hole directions.

The wiring setup will be found as a specimen circuit in Diagram 55 on p. 79. The long walls have one 17.5/3.34 m hairpin and two straight 9.75/2.97 m elements in the front wall and two 17.5/3.34 m hairpin elements in the back. The short walls each have two 9.75/2.97 m hairpins. One continuous 23/7 m length of coil is distributed in the four slots of the floor (this can be wound in two sections, of course, if too long for the mandrel). All figures refer to total overall length of wire as cut under Method, Step 19. The actual coils will take 2.5/.76 m less than these lengths, the remainder being used in the twisted tails.

Diag. 84. The frame for kiln in slotted or welded angle. Top and bottom inner members are inset to take asbestos across long side. The kiln box (without legs or connection housing at each end) measures 25/635 mm across the shorter sides, 31/790 mm along front and back, and 18/457 mm high.

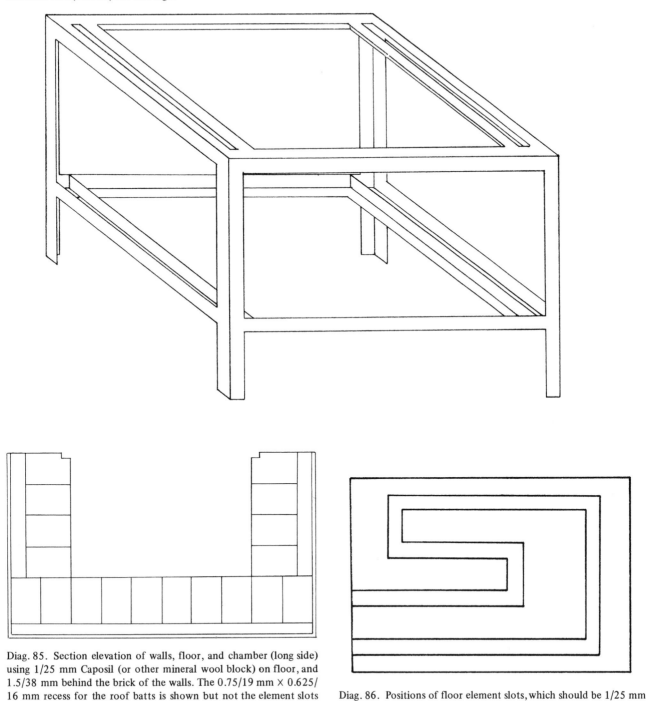

Diag. 85. Section elevation of walls, floor, and chamber (long side) using 1/25 mm Caposil (or other mineral wool block) on floor, and 1.5/38 mm behind the brick of the walls. The 0.75/19 mm × 0.625/ 16 mm recess for the roof batts is shown but not the element slots which are cut as described in Method step 20.

Diag. 86. Positions of floor element slots, which should be 1/25 mm wide and 0.75/19 mm deep.

KILN 2. TOP-LOADER 6.25/0.176 m³ TO FIRE TO 1280/2335°T

Chamber size: 30/762 mm × 18/257 mm × 20/508 mm high.
Exterior: 50/1270 mm × 32/813 mm × 38/965 mm high (with lid)
Top-loader: three circuits, total 14 kW, 240 V

MATERIALS

Lengths of Dexion metal angle or similar material (about 2.5/63 × 1.5/38 mm)	4	50/1270 mm
	4	31/787 mm Corners including 4/102 mm leg.
	4	30.5/774 mm
	4	32/813 mm
	2	43/1092 mm Floor cross stays.
Extra for hinged upper lid (Diagram 34)		200/5000 mm approximately
Asbestolux or similar material e.g., Transite.	2	48/1220 mm × 27/686 mm
(3 sheets 8/2.44 m × 4/1.22 m standard size)	2	43/1092 mm × 31/787 mm
	4	31/787 mm × 27/686 mm
	2	32/813 mm × 3/76 mm
White H.T. K25 Insulating bricks (also Lid, see below)	130	9/228 mm × 4.5/114 mm × 3/76 mm
	156	If only 2.5/64 mm thick.
Mineral wool block 2 inches thick to cover:		
floor	1	31/787 × 43/1092 mm
walls	2	43/1092 mm × 26/660 mm
	2	27/686 mm × 26/660 mm

N.B., If very heavy pots are to be fired it might be advisable to use 2 inches of brick or ceramic slab as the floor insulation layer.

Lid: Slabs or bricks K25 4.5/114 mm deep, to cover		43/1092 × 32/813 mm
2/51 mm mineral wool block or 3/76 mm insulating slabs		43/1092 × 32/813 mm
Kanthal or similar A1 wire 11 Awg or 13 Swg		375/115 m + spares (order 10 lbs)
Electrical sundries	33	line taps.
	5/1.5 m	asbestos covered wire, 4 mm
	1	three-phase 30 amp fuse box.
		wire, etc for installation.
Roof Batts (0.75/19 mm thick)	2	to cover 19.5/495 mm × 31.5/800 mm (total area)
Shelving and floor batts (Suggested)	10	16.5/420 mm × 14.5/370 mm × 0.625/16 mm
	4	16.5/420 mm × 20/45 mm × 0.5/13 mm
	4	16.5/420 mm × 9/228 mm × 0.5/13 mm

METHOD

1. Cut two of the larger sheets of Asbestolux (48 × 27 inches), two 31 × 27 inches, and a 43 × 31-inch floor sheet. N.B. *Use dust mask* when cutting or sweeping up asbestos.

2. Cut and assemble metal frame, placing cladding sheets in position before tightening up bolts. It will be necessary to cut or drill holes or slots in cladding where fitting is impeded by bolts. The outside dimensions of the kiln box are 44/1118 × 32/813 × 27/686 mm high. On each end are 3/76 mm connector covers, and the corner members extend 4/102 mm below to form legs. The leg members are situated on the outside corners of the whole frame, see Diagram 84 and Illustration 12.

3. Cut block or brick floor insulation and lay on asbestos sheet.

4. Set H.T. bricks on floor as in Diagram 88. Center 20 bricks 4.5/114 mm deep, outer layer 3/76 mm deep.

5. Cut and fit wall insulation slabs.

6. Cut and fit 4.5/114 mm thick H.T. brick walls giving a chamber 30/762 mm × 18/275 × 21/533 mm.

7. Check that the top surfaces of brick, insulation, and angle are level.

8. With a ruler and colored pencil or crayon mark the roof shelf recess and the element slots in wall and floor. Number or otherwise indicate position of the bricks.

9. Remove H.T. bricks which are marked, and cut grooves and recesses. Cut narrow upright slots for upright lengths of hairpin elements.

10. Reassemble bricks. Element wire hoops can be inserted at each layer to hold bricks in place but this is not absolutely necessary.

11. Drill holes for element tails. Angle holes as shown in Diagram 53.

12. Twist element tails and wind element coils on a 0.375/9 mm mandrel.

13. Stretch elements to fit slots.

14. Insert elements.

15. Connect up tails as in Diagram 89 with asbestos covered wire and line taps. Connect lines to switchbox and neutrals to appropriate terminal. In U.S. two 120 V lines are used to provide 240 V.

16. Take earth (grounding) wires from frame and connect.

17. Bolt 32/813 mm × 3/76 mm asbestos sheet onto top of element covers, and 32/813 × 27/686 mm end covers.

18. You should have left sufficient H.T. bricks for a 4.5/114 mm layer plus 2/51 mm insulating layer, a 43 × 31 asbestos sheet covers all. For general notes on lid see Small Kiln specifications and pp. 52 to 53 in the body of the book.

19. Elements: Wire lengths to be cut:

Circuit B straight	1	16/4.8 m length
Circuit B straight	1	11/3.35 m
Circuit R hairpin	1	24/7.32 m
Circuit Y (1) & B (1) hairpins	2	22/6.71 m
Circuit Y (1) & B (1) hairpins	2	19/5.8 m
Circuit B (2) hairpins	2	15/4.57 m
Circuit Y (3) hairpins	3	28/8.54 m
Circuit B (1) & R (3) hairpins	4	33/10.06 m

20. Slot positions (centers measured from the floor):
Long walls: 1.5/38 mm, 6/152 mm, 10/254 mm, 13.5/343 mm, 17/432 mm, 19.5/495 mm.
Short walls: 3/76 mm, 5/127 mm, 9/229 mm, 12.5/317 mm, 16/406 mm, 19.5/495 mm.
Floor measured from one lone side: 1.5/38 mm, 4.5174 mm, 7.5/190 mm, 10.5/267 mm, 13.5/343 mm, 16.5/419 mm.

21. Floor batts, two of the 16.5 × 14.5 shelves well supported on fireclay pellets about 0.25/6 mm above floor level.

The general layout of the frame for this kiln is similar to that of the previous smaller kiln and the photos on pp. 46-47. The outisde measurements of the kiln box (minus legs and connector covers) are 44/1117 mm × 815 mm × 686 mm. The extra weight of bricks, however, necessitates increased floor strength. Diagram 87 shows the layout of the metal angle cross members.

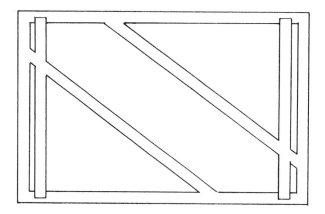

Diag. 87. Layout of base-level metal angle.

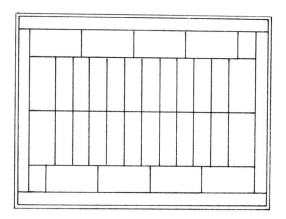

Diag. 88. Plan of brick, insulation, and asbestos. No brick cutting is needed if 3/76 mm bricks are used. The corner bricks can be set on end to fill the 3/76 mm × 4.5/114 mm gaps. The walls consist of eight bricks (in height) and a half brick, 9/228 mm × 4.5/114 mm × 1.5/12 mm. If the half bricks are used for the top level of the walls they can be cut with the 0.75/19 mm recess to take the roof batts. The first element slot will then be cut into the first full size brick beneath it (see similar arrangement, without recess, in the specifications for a front-loader, Diagram 95).

126

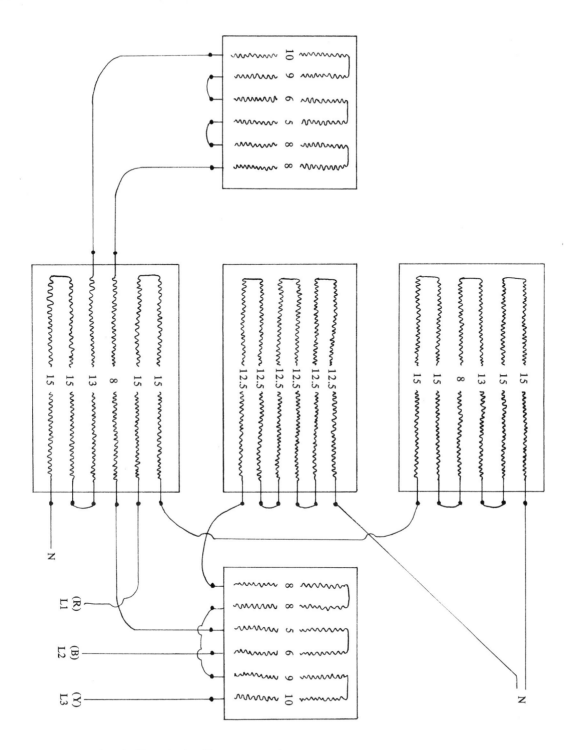

Diag. 89. Wiring diagram for 14 kW top-loader. Elements are to be wound as indicated. As mentioned in the text, the lower middle level of a top-loading kiln is usually the hottest spot if all elements are equal. An attempt has been made here to balance this tendency and also to compensate for heat loss through the lid.

KILN 3. FRONT-LOADER

10.4/0.3 m³ for earthenware to fire to 1150/2100°T
Chamber size: 21/533 mm × 28.5/724 mm × 30/762 mm high
Exterior: 33/838 mm × 41/1041 mm × 44.5/1130 mm high plus 21.5/546 mm legs
Front-loader: four circuits, total 16 kW, 240 V

MATERIALS

Metal Angle		4	66/1676 mm
slotted 2.5/63 × 1.5/38 mm		2	31.5/800 mm
welded 2/51 × 2/51 mm		7	32.5/825 mm
total about 100/30 m		8	41/1040 mm
		6	18/457 mm
		2	53/1346 mm
Asbestos cladding (or some	sides	2	43.5/1105 × 40.5/1029 mm
may be metal): Transite.	back inside	1	31.5/800 × 43.5/1105 mm
	back outside	1	32/813 × 44/1118 mm
	top	1	33/838 × 41/1040 mm
	floor	1	32/813 × 38/965 mm
	front (sides)	2	43.5/1105 × 3/76 mm
	front (center)	1	42.5/1080 × 25/635 mm
White H. T. K23 Insulating bricks.		255	9/228 mm × 4.5/114 mm × 3/76 mm
		305	if only 2.5/63 mm thick
Mineral wool block 1/25	back		32/813 mm × 44/1118 mm
mm thick to cover:	sides	2 areas	34.5/876 mm × 37.5/952 mm
Loose fill for roof (ceramic fiber, broken up mineral wool block or H.T. brick, alumina bubbles, or vermiculite)			one bag.
Kanthal A1 wire 14 Swg or 12 Awg			450/114m + spares (order 9 lbs)
Electrical sundries:			
line taps		33	
asbestos-covered 4 mm wire		10/3 m	
three-pole 40A switch gear etc.			
Shelving, (suggested):		12	19/482 mm × 13.5/343 mm
0.5/13 mm thick		8	9.5/240 mm × 13.5/343 mm

METHOD

1. Cut and assemble frame, fitting side, floor, and inner back asbestos as you go. See Diagrams 90, 91, and 92. N.B. If frame is to be welded, some of the cross stays can be omitted. If sheet metal is used as cladding do *not* use it for back walls. Use asbestos where element tails pierce walls in all situations.

2. Cut and fit insulation layers. It would be beneficial to adhere mineral block to asbestos with odd spots of heat-proof glue such as that sold for ceramic fiber. A layer of bright foil between asbestos and block would give added insulation but do *not* lay any across the back.

3. Mock up walls and floor and mark and cut element slots between each layer (see Diagram 95). Bricks could well be numbered. Only the fourth join up (from floor surface level) in the back wall is not cut. See wiring Diagram 97 for type and position of elements.

4. Lay back wall bricks to roof level, followed by first brick of wall to roof level. Set floor and surround, and complete walls. Introduce narrow strips of asbestos side-front trims when this point is reached.

5. Cut and set angled 'scewbacks' for roof. Set roof bricks. The kiln would be firmer if bricks were mortared. This is not essential for the walls but recommended for the roof. An air/heat-setting H.T. mortar for 1200/2190°T should be used. The bricks must be dunked in water before mortaring. Use *very* thinly. Leave 0.5/13 mm gap as shown in diagram 96 between front brick level and angle iron to accommodate asbestos 'draught shield'. Fill space above roof with loose fill level with top angle.

6. Drill holes for element tails.

7. Twist ends and wind elements, 7/178 mm tails if line taps are used: at least 10/255 mm for connection panels. In the latter case add 3/76 mm to overall element wire lengths.

8. Stretch elements to appropriate slot lengths and connect into four circuits as in Diagram 97.

9. Attach earth (grounding) wire to frame and connect.

10. Bolt back and top asbestos sheets into place.

11. Cut elements: 4 at 31/9.45 m
                   12   27/8.23 m

12. Element slots are located at every level of brick joints—35 slots in all.

13. Floor batts: 2 19/482 mm × 13.5/343 mm × 0.5/13 mm see Shelving.

14. When the kiln is ready to fire and all door bricks are in place, the remaining asbestos sheet is introduced under the top angle and drops into bottom angle gap. An inch of packing will stop the sheet falling out of the top slot. It will be necessary to bolt two handles (metal of course) onto the face of the asbestos in order to handle it into position. The kiln will then be completely cased in sheet material excluding draughts. One or more spyholes can be cut and marked on the appropriate brick which is likewise drilled and reamed out.

15. No ventilation is allowed for in this design. Two spyholes, top and bottom, would provide some draught. The kiln could be dried by switching on before all the bricks are set in the doorway. If the type of work necessitates ventilation during firing, then one or two holes should be drilled in the center roof bricks and through the top asbestos sheet. A ceramic funnel and stopper may then be made to set in the ventilation hole to prevent the loose fill dropping into the kiln.

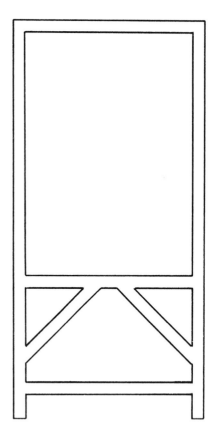

Diag. 90. Front view showing positions of cross stays.

129

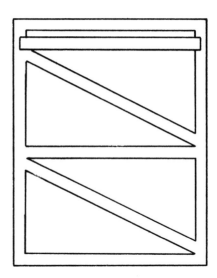

Diag. 92. Plan of floor-supporting angle iron showing inset inner back member which supports the back wall of the kiln and leaves 3 ins at the rear for element connections. The principle is similar to that of the top-loader Frame Illus. 12.

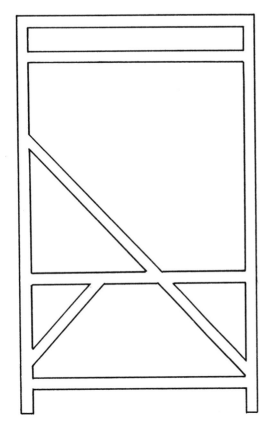

Diag. 91. Side view showing cross stays and extra length of angle to take the outward pressure from roof bricks.

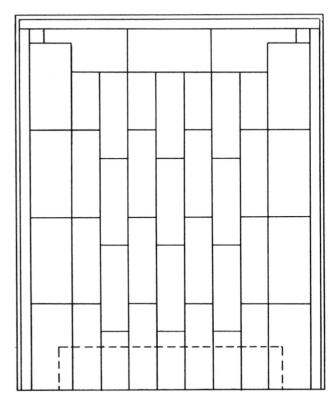

Diag. 93. Floor and walls. Arrangement of bricks. Dotted line indicates 4.5/114 mm thickness of bricks which would be built up (dry), as the door, at each firing. See also Diagram 96.

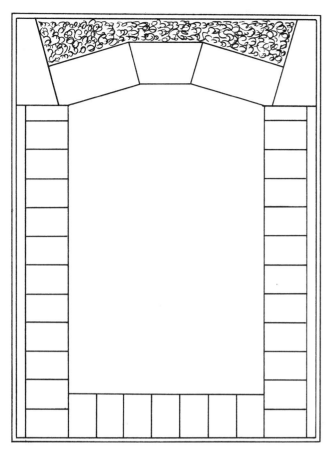

Diag. 94. Section elevation showing position of bricks and suggested roof construction. The roof could alternatively be built of arch bricks over a former.

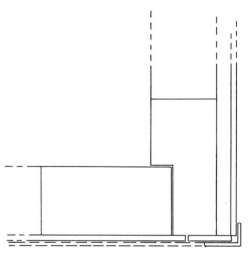

Diag. 96. Detail of door brick recess cut in each of the front wall bricks. The front asbestos sheet is also shown in place. The side asbestos strips are kept permanently in position.

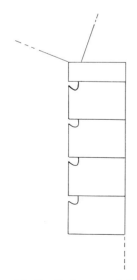

Diag. 95. Detail of system of slot cutting.

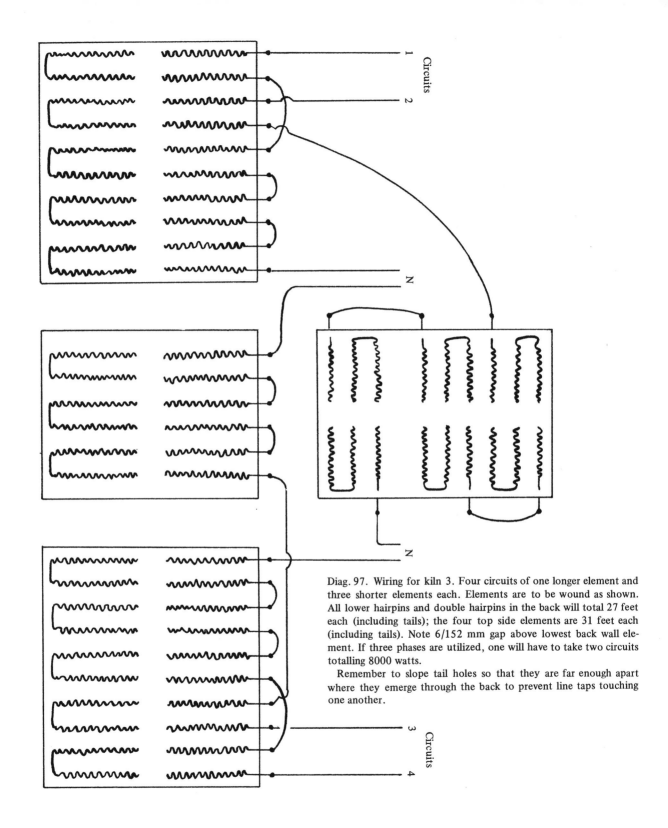

Diag. 97. Wiring for kiln 3. Four circuits of one longer element and three shorter elements each. Elements are to be wound as shown. All lower hairpins and double hairpins in the back will total 27 feet each (including tails); the four top side elements are 31 feet each (including tails). Note 6/152 mm gap above lowest back wall element. If three phases are utilized, one will have to take two circuits totalling 8000 watts.

Remember to slope tail holes so that they are far enough apart where they emerge through the back to prevent line taps touching one another.

KILN 4. SILICON-CARBIDE FRONT-LOADER

30/763 × 18/457 × 24/610 mm to fire to 1350/2460°T
Designed and drawn by Labheat (Peter Taylor) Ironbridge,
England.

MATERIALS, APPROXIMATE

Asbestolux or similar material:		
(Transite) 0.125/3.5 mm thick	1 sheet	37/940 mm × 39/990 mm
	2	38/965 mm × 39/990 mm
	1	38/965 mm × 37/940 mm
	2	39/990 mm × 5/127 mm
White insulating H.T. bricks K25	175	9/228 × 4.5/114 × 3/76 mm
	66	Arch bricks
		or equivalent plain bricks if alternative system is used.
Red Diatomaceous bricks.	220	
Metal angle (slotted)	4 lengths	37/940 mm
	4	38/965 mm
	4	39/990 mm
18-gauge sheet metal	2 pieces	39/990 mm × 12/305 mm
Elements		12 SiC rods to span 24/610 hot section. Clips, braid, etc.

N.B. This list is a guide to materials required. Consult Labheat for checking precise details.

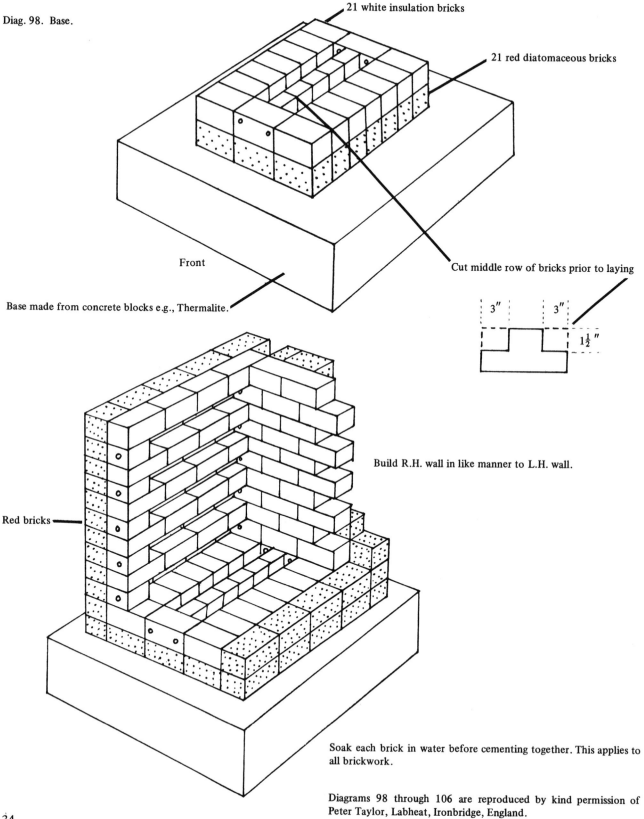

Diag. 98. Base.

21 white insulation bricks

21 red diatomaceous bricks

Cut middle row of bricks prior to laying

3″   3″

1½″

Front

Base made from concrete blocks e.g., Thermalite.

Build R.H. wall in like manner to L.H. wall.

Red bricks

Soak each brick in water before cementing together. This applies to all brickwork.

Diagrams 98 through 106 are reproduced by kind permission of Peter Taylor, Labheat, Ironbridge, England.

Diag. 99. Sides and back.

Build the sides and back directly on the base. Allow to dry before constructing roof, OR support sides when building roof.

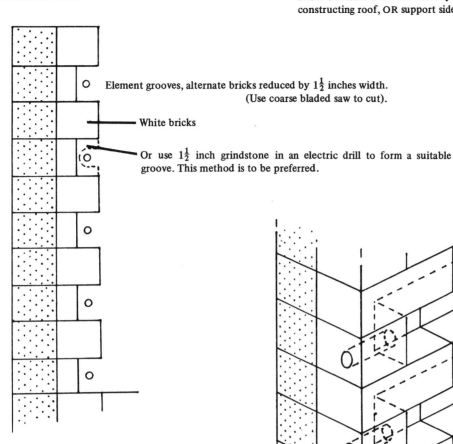

○ Element grooves, alternate bricks reduced by $1\frac{1}{2}$ inches width.
(Use coarse bladed saw to cut).

White bricks

Or use $1\frac{1}{2}$ inch grindstone in an electric drill to form a suitable groove. This method is to be preferred.

Section through side walls.

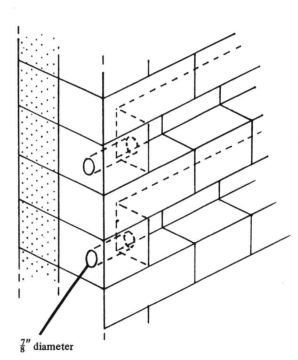

$\frac{7}{8}''$ diameter

Detail to front (inside) face of side walls. Drill $\frac{7}{8}$-inch diameter holes at front and rear of kiln, align holes using $\frac{3}{4}$-inch diameter dowel rod.

Slide elements carefully into position after completion of kiln prior to *final stage* and pack holes loosely with ceramic fiber around element ends.

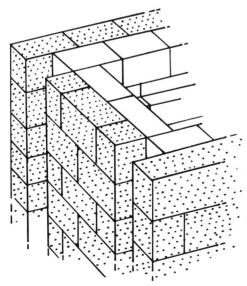

Detail to rear of kiln back wall

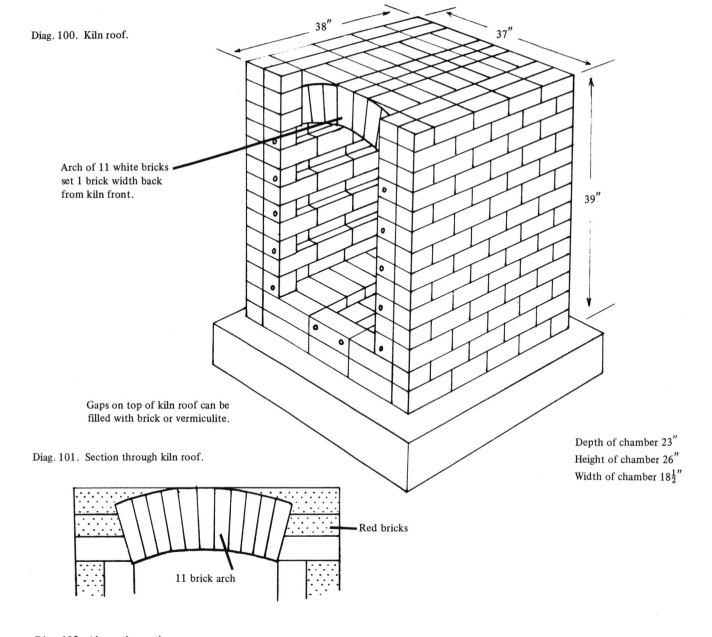

Diag. 100. Kiln roof.

38″ 37″

39″

Arch of 11 white bricks set 1 brick width back from kiln front.

Gaps on top of kiln roof can be filled with brick or vermiculite.

Depth of chamber 23″
Height of chamber 26″
Width of chamber $18\frac{1}{2}$″

Diag. 101. Section through kiln roof.

Red bricks

11 brick arch

Diag. 102. Alternative section.

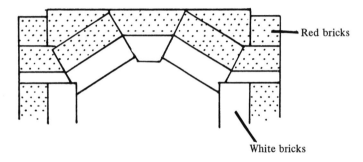

Red bricks

White bricks

Diag. 103. Element covers.

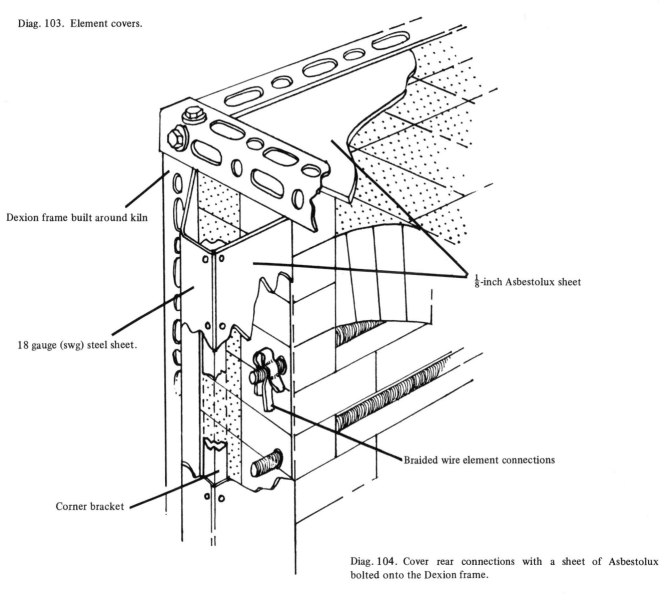

Dexion frame built around kiln

$\frac{1}{8}$-inch Asbestolux sheet

18 gauge (swg) steel sheet.

Braided wire element connections

Corner bracket

Diag. 104. Cover rear connections with a sheet of Asbestolux bolted onto the Dexion frame.

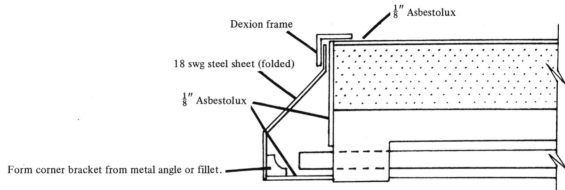

Dexion frame

$\frac{1}{8}''$ Asbestolux

18 swg steel sheet (folded)

$\frac{1}{8}''$ Asbestolux

Form corner bracket from metal angle or fillet.

Diag. 105. Completed kiln.

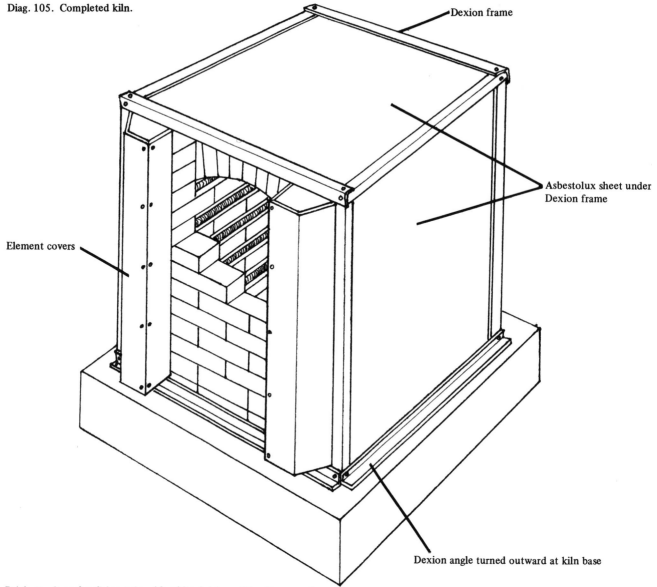

Dexion frame

Asbestolux sheet under
Dexion frame

Element covers

Dexion angle turned outward at kiln base

Brick up door for firing using 12 white bricks cutting the second
from top layer to fit the arch.

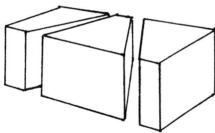

Diag. 106. A spyhole can be formed by cutting a brick in three, as
shown here.

138

KILN 5. RAKU KILN

Chamber size: 13.5/345 mm X 13.5345 mm X 10.5/265 mm high.

Exterior size: 20.5/520 X 25/635 X 20/510 mm high.

Load 3,000 W, 12.5 A, at 240 V

MATERIALS

Angle iron, 1.5/38 mm X 1.5/38 mm, or thereabouts

4 lengths   25/635 mm
7 lengths   19.5/495 mm
4 lengths   20/500 mm or to height required

Note: the kiln illustrated in photos 51 and 52 has extra lengths of angle at the base to which are fixed blocks of timber to take casters, making it more mobile

Asbestolux, or similar material, 0.25/6 mm thick, or thereabouts (thicker if $2\frac{1}{2}$ inch bricks are used).

1 sheet 18.5/470 mm square (2 sheets if kiln is to be used for biscuit)
2 sheets 25/635 mm X 13.5/345 mm
4 sheets 18.5/470 mm X 13.5/345 mm

Brick K23

29 'straights' (squares)
  2 18/457 X 4.5/115 X 9/229 mm slabs for roof, or 12 (16) more bricks

Elements: (Wired as a single circuit) 114/35.75 m of 15 swg or 13 awg Kanthal A1 wire wound into (including 5/125 mm turn-back for tails:

4 hairpins each 13.75/4.2 m
2 double hairpins each 21.75/6.63 m
1 straight 20.75/6.3 m

Connectors:

14 line taps, or ceramic/brass connectors would last quite well below 1000/1830°T
4/1.2 m of asbestos covered 2.5 mm wire

This kiln is suitable for firings up to 1050/1920°T only: enamels, raku, biscuit, or low-fired earthenwares. It has a very fast temperature climb up to about 700/1300°T.

The kiln is assembled to form 3-inch thick walls and floor (2.5/63 mm if thinner U.S. bricks are used). The method is similar to Kilns 1 and 2. For normal firing (not raku), if 18/457 mm slabs cannot be obtained for the roof, then it will be necessary to rebate the top bricks as Kiln 1 to take a batt (which, in this case, need be only 0.5/12 mm or 0.375/9 mm thick). A 4.5/115 mm thick roof is then formed from ordinary bricks.

The use of 2.5/63 mm bricks for the chamber will give a slightly larger volume and, of course, less insulation. A thicker asbestos outer skin is therefore recommended. The outside will still get fairly hot when 1050/1920°T firings are in progress.

Suppliers

U.S.

Babcock and Wilcox, Old Savannah Road, Augusta, Georgia, 30903. Ceramic Fiber products, refractories, and mineral wool blocks.

The Carborundum Company, Ltd., P.O.B. 339, Niagara Falls, N.Y. 14302 and district offices. Ceramic fibers (Fiberfrax), Globar SiC elements, silicon carbide shelves, etc.

Electro Refractories, 18765, Fibreglass Road, Huntington Beach, California 92647

A. P. Green Refractories Company, Mexico, Missouri. District, and International Offices throughout U.S.

Johns-Manville, 22 East 40th Street, New York, New York 10016. Ceramic fibers and refractories.

Kanthal Corporation, Bethel, Connecticut (and other centers in various countries). Kanthal wire, etc.

The Norton Company Refractories Division. Makers of 'Crystolon' SiC elements. Worcester, Mass. 01606

Superamics. P.O.B. 8363, Madera Beach, Florida 33738. Suppliers of ceramic fiber blanket, etc.

M. Wikey Company, 1010 Martin Avenue, Santa Clara, California 95050. Range of ceramic supplies and equipment. See also Bibliography.

U.K.

Acme Marls Ltd., Clough Street, Hanley, S-o-T. Staffs. Kiln shelves and supports.

Cape Insulation Ltd., Stirling, Scotland. Makers of Caposil and Sindanyo Asbestos.

The Carborundum Company, Ltd., Mill Lane, Rainford, St. Helens, WA11 8LP. Ceramic fibers (Fiberfrax), Globar SiC elements, silicon carbide shelves, etc.

Dexion Ltd., Dexion House, Empire Way, Wembley, Middlesex. Makers of slotted angle. Can provide catalog and booklets.

F. F. Refractories, 24, Farrow Road off Shady Lane, Great Barr, Birmingham, B44 9HE. All refractories and ceramic fiber.

Gibbons Ltd., Dibdale Works, Lower Gornal, Near Dudley, Worcestershire. High quality refractories but, like most large manufacturers today, are unenthusiastic about small orders.

A. P. Green Refractories Company, Green Company House, High Street, Slough, Bucks.

Hall and Pickles, Ltd. Wire Division, Ecclesfield, Sheffield. Kanthal resistance wire.

Mike Harris, School House, Dyrrham, Wilts. Advice on kilns and supplier of pyrometers and other control equipment.

Harris and Bailey, 105, Lower Addicombe Road, Croydon, Surrey. Bricks and refractory cements.

Labheat, 56 Hodge Bower, Ironbridge, Salop. Peter Taylor will supply many materials in small quantities. He offers materials and advice on installing SiC rod kilns without voltage transformers.

Lafarge Aluminous Cement Company, Ltd. P.O.B. 13, 730, London Road, Grays, RM16 1NJ.

C. Mayman, FGF (Aston) Ltd., 37, Princip Street, Birmingham, 4. Suppliers of Caposil.

Moler Products Ltd., Hythe Works, Colchester, Essex, CO2 8JU, refractory bricks and insulation materials.

Morganite Ceramic Fibre Ltd., Neston, Wirrel, L64 3TR. Makers of Triton Kaowool products.

Morganite Electroheat Ltd., Inveralmond, Perth, Scotland. Makers and suppliers of 'Crystolon' and 'Crusilite' SiC elements. 'Crystolon' is a registered Trade Mark of The Norton Company, United States.

Principal Refractories Ltd., Silver End, Trading Estate, Brettell Lane, Brierly Hill, Staffs, DY5 3ZA. Retailers of refractories and a wide range of cements and castables.

Satchwell-Sunvic Ltd., Watling Street, Motherwell, Lanarkshire, ML1 3SA. Energy regulators.

Sifam Electrical Instrument Company, Ltd., Woodland Road, Torquay TQ2 7AY. Pyrometer indicators and controls.

Most of the larger ceramic supply companies (Wengers, Ferro, Podmores, Cress, Harrison Meyer, etc.) supply heat-measuring and control equipment for electric kilns, shelves, etc.

Bibliography

Anderton, Pamela. *Changing to the Metric System* (1972). HMSO, London. A useful conversion reference book.

Ceramic Review, 7 Marshall St., London W1V 1FD. Has published several articles on electric kilns including a simple SiC rod kiln.

Colson, Frank A. *Kiln Building with Space-Age Materials* (1975). Van Nostrand Reinhold, New York. The only book to date dealing with ceramic fiber as a potter's kiln material; does not discuss electric kilns.

Fraser, Harry. *Kilns and Kiln Firing for the Craft Potter* (1969). Pitman, London. The development and use of kilns with an emphasis on electric kilns.

Kanthal, AB. *Kanthal Handbook* (1970). Kanthal Corp., Bethel, Connecticut. Also from Hall & Pickles, Ltd. Wire Division, Ecclesfield, Sheffield, England. An invaluable reference book on resistance wire.

Miller, Henry, A. *Basic Electrical Principles, SI Units* (1972). Edward Arnold, London. A short and very readable book on the theory of electricity and its practical application in wiring systems, etc.

——. *Basic Electrical Principles and Electrical Principles 2*, 2 Vols. (1975). Herman Publishing, 45 Newbury St., Boston, Massachusetts 02116

Olsen, Fred. *The Kiln Book* (1973). Keramos Books, P.O.B. 2315, La Puenta, California 91746. A chapter on building electric kilns although his conclusion seems to be—buy one!

Rhodes, Daniel. *Kilns: Design, Construction and Operation* (1968). Chilton, Radnor, Pennsylvania, and Pitman, London. A short chapter on electric kiln building.

Thorp, Harold. *Basic Pottery for the Student* (1969). Alec Tiranti, London, and (1974) St. Martin, New York. Includes instruction on building a simple front-loading electric kiln.

Thring, M. W. *Science of Flames and Furnaces* (1952). Chapman & Hall, London. The classic book on heat and furnaces, mostly fuel-burning.

Wikey, M. *Calibrating and Calculating the Electric Kiln* (1974). Marshall Craft, 1001 Martin Ave., Santa Clara, California 95050. A fairly exhaustive book on its subject, but I find his watt-loss figures questionable.

Index